Alexandra Bastedo is an actress best kno
the cult TV series *The Champions*. She
RSPCA branch, vice-president of the Bren
Patron of Sidlesham Cat and Rabbit R
Persian Cat Rescue, Wild Life Aid and the
She runs a sanctuary of her own with one hundred and eighty animals and has recently started a company called Pet Nutrition Concepts, which provides Feline and Canine Care Vitamins, Minerals, Anti-oxidants and Essential Oils. She writes her own pet nutrition column for *Healthy Eating* magazine.

Jeannie Kemnitzer comes from Santa Barbara, California, but settled permanently in England in 1972 when she began working at the Chichester Festival Theatre. After a ten-year spell at a publishing firm in London, Jeannie now specialises as a freelance secretary/researcher in theatre and publishing. She also designs and makes exclusive knitwear, as well as creating dream-catchers.

Also by Alexandra Bastedo

Beware Dobermanns, Donkeys and Ducks

By Alexandra Bastedo and Jeannie Kemnitzer

The Healthy Cat Book

THE HEALTHY DOG BOOK

THE NATURAL WAY TO
CANINE CARE AND CUISINE

ALEXANDRA BASTEDO
and
JEANNIE KEMNITZER

First published in paperback in Great Britain in 1999
by Robson Books, 10 Blenheim Court, Brewery Road,
London N7 9NT

A member of the Chrysalis Group plc

Disclaimer: The authors and publishers shall have neither liability nor responsibility for any dog or person with respect to any loss or damage caused, directly or indirectly, by the information contained in this book. All information was correct at the time of going to press.

British Library Cataloguing in Publication Data
A catalogue record for this title is available from the British Library

ISBN 1 86105 267 7

Printed and bound in Great Britain by Creative Print and Design Wales, Ebbw Vale

I want my boy to have a dog,
Or maybe two or three.
He'll learn from him much easier
Than he will learn from me.
A dog will teach him how to love
And bear no grudge or hate;
I'm not so good at that myself,
But a dog will do it straight.

Traditional

CONTENTS

PREFACE

I was always very impressed by the longevity of Alexandra Bastedo's many animals and she told me this was due to the vitamin/mineral supplements and antioxidants that her doctor had prescribed for herself but which she gave to her animals as well. She said it was a shame that more good supplements were not available for dogs and cats.

I read the extensive *Canine Care and Cuisine* book that Alexandra had written with Jeannie Kemnitzer and was happy to give it my approval, having been impressed by the way our fussy dogs and those of my parents eagerly devoured Jeannie's healthy homemade dog food.

In cooking food some of the vitamin values are lost and I recommended to Alexandra and Jeannie the addition of a selection of vitamins, minerals, antioxidants and essential oils. They in turn asked me to advise on my formulas, which I have done, and which have been used in creating the Canine Care Range. All the vitamin/mineral supplements, antioxidants, essential oils, and dog food recipes have been tried on patients and our dogs.

MARK ELLIOTT BVSc VetMFHom MRCVS
Kingley Veterinary Centre, Lavant, West Sussex

INTRODUCTION

The inevitable question, 'Whatever made you write a dogs' cookbook?' keeps cropping up. Well, total coincidence. In the summer of 1993 my friends, Amanda and Robert Daws, acquired a little cross-breed puppy which they named Tippy. They spent most of the summer down on a farm near Chichester while Amanda was appearing at the Chichester Festival Theatre in *Getting Married*. Tippy spent *her* days roaming freely in the fields with the other farm dogs, so the following spring, when Tippy found herself staying with Amanda's parents, Dorothy Tutin and Derek Waring, in London, she had trouble distinguishing the freedom of the country from the confines of the city. A tempting squirrel on Putney Common was too much to resist and off shot Tippy in pursuit, heading straight towards a relatively unused road. Unfortunately that day there *was* a car. The driver tried desperately to avoid hitting Tippy, but Tippy ended up in intensive care with only a 20 per cent chance of survival. After a permanent steel plate was inserted into her front leg, however, she was on the road to recovery. So what does one send a dog as a convalescence present? Home-made dog biscuits, of course! The dogs in Singleton were most obliging in sampling my various attempts at formulating a recipe that worked, and an enthusiastic thank-you letter from Tippy put the seal on Tippy Daws Dog Biscuits.

A year later I met Alexandra Bastedo while working for her husband, Patrick Garland, the theatre producer and writer. One couldn't live in the Chichester area without hearing about Alexandra's animal sanctuary and her love of animals particularly since *Beware Dobermanns, Donkeys and Ducks*, her first book, had just been published. What I hadn't been prepared for was Alexandra's vast knowledge of diets for animals, their nutritional needs, and various remedies (particularly homoeopathic ones) for ailing pets. Unbeknown to me she had been purchasing my Tippy Daws Dog Biscuits at my outlet at Pump Bottom Farm, wondering who on earth would make home-made dog biscuits!

From an early age I got a lot of pleasure out of concocting original recipes and many people have admired my ingenuity at preparing delicious food. Perhaps it's in the genes. My father was an excellent cook, declaring that 'anyone who can read can cook' but at the same time rarely followed a recipe – his motto being 'improvise with existing'! My three brothers, Luis Jr., Paul and Bryan, inherited the same flair and have become extremely creative cooks. My mother always made specially cooked meals for our dogs; hence many of the recipes that appear in this book have been handed down from generation to generation. To this day – forty years on – whenever I meet up with my school-friend, Judith Burnett, she never fails to remind and tease me that at the age of seven I used to bring a pocketful of kibble to school as a snack (charcoal flavour was my favourite . . .). The one drawback or advantage, whichever way one looks at it, was that I could never share my treats because nobody else liked to eat dog biscuits!

Jeannie Kemnitzer

JEANNIE KEMNITZER
Singleton, West Sussex

FOREWORD

For some time I have espoused the practice of preventative medicine, both for myself and for my animals, and my thinking has also naturally turned to their nutritional requirements. A homoeopathic doctor once said to me: 'If you put the right petrol in your car it runs perfectly and if you put the right food into a person or animal they too will function properly.' Unfortunately, that still doesn't take into account the modern world of pollution, chemicals, hormones and antibiotics; so we have included a holistic section advising on antioxidants, vitamins, minerals, essential oils, homoeopathy and herbs to counteract their harmful effects.

I first heard of Jeannie through her Tippy Daws Dog Biscuits which were being sold at Pump Bottom Farm near Chichester. They were made of Singleton stoneground wholemeal flour, bulghur wheat, oats with bran, yeast, fresh stock, dried skimmed milk, parsley, garlic and free range eggs – all thoroughly healthy ingredients which were immediately wolfed up by my three Dobermanns. The trouble was that Pump Bottom Farm soon sold out and when I went in search of the mysterious 'Jeannie', I discovered she was in fact working for my husband!

When we met we immediately found we had a lot in common including North American ancestry and a great love of animals and concern for their welfare. However, there is one particular difference – Jeannie is a superb cook (which I am not) but through my animal sanctuary of 170 animals I do know a lot about the nutritional needs of animals at different stages of their lives and through different illnesses. The majority of canned products include additives and colourants and the makers are not obliged to itemise the ingredients. If you examine the small print on the tins you will find the contents described as 'meat and animal derivatives' or 'meat and animal by-products' and sometimes even 'vegetable derivatives'. Could somebody please tell us what a vegetable derivative is?!

We believe in this modern age there is a real need for tasty nutritional food for dogs whether they are carnivore, vegetarian, vegan or macrobiotic. In *Canine Care and Cuisine* Jeannie and I offer you a broad spectrum of delicious recipes which, together with nutritional supplements designed by our vet Mark Elliott, aim to keep your pet in optimum health.

Alexandra Bastedo

ALEXANDRA BASTEDO
Almodington, West Sussex

ACKNOWLEDGEMENTS

Grateful thanks to:

Mark Elliott BVSc VetMFHom MRCVS, our homoeopathic vet and Nick Thompson and Peter Brown, his associates, for all their advice, care and approval and for helping to make my dogs long-lived, healthy senior citizens.

Francis Hunter Vet MF Hom MRCVS, chairman of the British Homoeopathic Association for sharing his extensive knowledge with us.

Tim Couzens BvetMed MRCVS VetMFHom, for all his useful healthy tips.

The Reverend David MacLeod for all his kindness and help.

Jessie Howling and Bob Hutchins without whose special constant help my animal rescue operation would not be possible.

The Kennel Club Library staff, especially Elaine Camroux, for being so helpful with research.

The Chichester Library staff, especially Emma Sparkes, for help with research and tracking down books.

The staff at Hammicks book shop in Chichester, especially Carmen Fernandez, for her enthusiasm about the project and ordering endless books.

Sue Martin for her illustrations.

Pollyanna Pickering for providing extra animal artwork.

Tim Faulkner for widening our knowledge of dogs in art.

All the charities, associations, companies, private enterprises and private individuals for allowing us to include their details in the Appropriate Addresses and Notable Names sections.

All the authors and publishers connected with the literary quotes featured throughout the book.

ALEXANDRA'S DOGS

Noddy	A black poodle who had epileptic fits.
Huston	A Yorkshire Terrier who would only cross the road on zebra crossings.
Charlies	The Yorkshire Terrier friend of Huston's, adopted at the age of five.
Blue	A black Dobermann whose favourite shop was Allen's the butchers in Mayfair.
Ben	The white retriever who developed fits due to a brain tumour.
Sophie	A brown Dobermann who would perform 'dead dog' for any choice morsel.
Baranaby	Sophie's black and tan son who was very bright.
Kipling	Sophie's black and tan son who became very ill after a vaccination.
Daisy	The brown Dobermann bitch adopted at seven who lived until thirteen aided by various vitamins.
Little Dorrit	Daisy's brown daughter who developed skin problems after walking through a potato field that had recently been sprayed.
Roscoe	A black and tan Dobermann rescued at seven having been abanded in kennels for seven months.

This list does not include the numerous dogs that have briefly passed through before being re-homed.

WHAT I LOVE ABOUT MY DOG TIPPY

My dog's liquorice snout,
Her ears that flap about.
Doleful eyes that look
Into my soul
And plead or comfort
With one glance.

I walk through the door,
She greets me barking
Before starting her
Welcome home dance.

The way she takes up
Half my bed,
Yawning at full stretch.
And she brings back tennis balls
Without me saying fetch.

My squirrel chasing,
Leaping fencing,
Running through the vale.
My fearless hound,
Who with one bound
Still lives to tell the tale.

My dog, my companion,
My confidante, my friend.
I will always love you
Till the very end.

Amanda Barton-Chapple

CANINE CARE

HOLISTIC HEALING

'Our food should be our medicine and our medicine should be our food.'

Hippocrates

Canine holistic healing is the treatment of dogs with natural remedies: homoeopathy, herbs and nutrition. A qualified vet should be consulted if needed and the use of prescribed drugs or surgery carried out when necessary, but in my opinion far too often antibiotics and steroids are used when a natural remedy may suffice. Too much chemical medication can lower the immune system and destroy the natural flora in the gut. If the right foods are given with the correct nutrients, together with preventative homoeopathic and herbal remedies, unless there is a genetic fault, serious injury or disease, I believe that vet bills can be kept to a minimum.

My veterinary gurus are George MacLeod, who was at the forefront of homoeopathy when I came across him seventeen years ago, Francis Hunter, Dr Richard Pitcairn, and my own vet, Mark Elliott. With their help and with reference to their books (in the bibliography at the back of the book) I have compiled the section on homoeopathy. I swear also by Juliette de Bairacli Levy's and Diane Stein's herbal remedies which can work very well with dogs. Any cooking should not be overdone as the vitamin content will be destroyed if heat levels are high. Dr Pitcairn and Mark Elliott both recommend adding canine vitamins and minerals to a dog's diet; these should be added at the end of the cooking process.

A dog's health is immediately visible in its coat, and dandruff or lacklustre dry hair may indicate incorrect proportions of protein, fat and carbohydrate in its diet and a possible vitamin deficiency. Worms can also seriously affect the normal food absorption. I recommend Droncit, and Panacur which also treats giardia in weaned puppies. Another possible sign of worms is when the dog has consistently loose stools. A possible alternative to a wormer recommended by a vet is Juliette de Bairacli Levy's herbal wormers which should be given twice a year. A meat-only diet is deficient in phosphorus and calcium and will cause diarrhoea, fragile bones and joint problems, together with a dull coat. Dogs need protein, fat and carbohydrates the same as humans. Vitamins are also essential to maintain the health of your dog and vitamin C supplements are always beneficial, particularly for bigger dogs. Other necessary minerals are calcium, copper, iodine, iron, magnesium, manganese, phosphorus, potassium, selenium, sodium and zinc. Salt in tiny amounts is needed to prevent water retention or dehydration, but dogs with heart disease need a diet particularly low in salt.

Homoeopathy stems from the Greek 'homo' meaning same and 'pathos' meaning suffering – i.e. like treats like. My Dobermann, Little Dorrit, developed a nasty red rash on her chest after we had gone walking along a footpath through potato fields three days after they had been sprayed with chemicals. Conventional vets prescribed steroids, antibiotics and various ointments which improved the condition temporarily, but it always returned. Finally I called in Nick Thompson, who works with Mark Elliott, and he made me call the farmer to find out which chemicals had been used. Fortunately, the farmer was obliging and said that it was a tin-based spray which stayed on the potato plants for three weeks. The vet asked for a sample of the spray which the farmer agreed to give him. 'That way,' said Nick, 'we can treat like with like and create a pill which may help.' My bitch had also become allergic to wheat but fortunately a combination of diet and homoeopathy has now cured her.

Samuel Hahnemann, the founder of homoeopathy, said that homoeopathy was curative rather than preventative and that one had to abide by the laws of nature. Homoeopathy could not cure if the underlying cause was bad nutrition.

KEY HOMOEOPATHIC REMEDIES

CONDITION	REMEDY
Abscesses	*Streptococcus* is a principal remedy. *Hepar Sulph* is for infection and suppuration. According to Francis Hunter it could be considered the homoeopathic equivalent of an antibiotic as its action is principally directed at infected tissues and glands. *Silicea* should be considered if a splinter or foreign body may be involved.
Alopecia (Hair loss)	*Thallium Acetas* and *Thyroidinum* are the major remedies.
Anaemia	According to George MacLeod this is difficult to treat homoeopathically. He suggests: *Arsenicum Album* which may help damage done to red blood cells. *Crotalus Horr* and *Lachesis* where there are liver problems or jaundice. *Cinchona* can supplement other remedies where there is weakness and lethargy due to loss of body fluid. *Ferrum Metallicum* or *Ferrum Muriaticum* should be given in case of an iron deficiency. *Aconitum, Arnica, Ficus Religiosa* and *Ipecac* are just some of the remedies suggested by George MacLeod. Note: Anaemia can be caused by heavy infestations of fleas
Anal Glands	*Arsenicum Album, Graphites, Hepar Sulph, Merc Sol, Natrum Mur* and *Silicea* are the best remedies.
Anxiety, fear and aggression	Some of the main remedies are:

Aconite, Anacardium, Arg Nit, Arsenicum Album, Belladonna, Gelsemium, Hyoscyamus, Ignatia, Lachesis, Nux Vom, Phosphorus, Pulsatilla, Staphysagria, Stramonium.

Arthritis

Rhus Tox is particularly good where restlessness is a problem.
Bryonia is often beneficial in chronic arthritis and can be followed by *Rhus Tox* or the remedies may be alternated once or twice daily.

Bites and stings

For wasp stings use *Ledum Palustre*, bee and nettle stings, hives and rashes use *Urtica Urens*, bee stings and bites, *Apis Mel*, for snake bites use *Hypericum* and for snake and insect bites use *Echinacea*.

Bronchitis

Bryonia is also good for chest infections and many kinds of cough. Other remedies which may be appropriate are:
Antimonium Tart for frothy mucus.
Apis Mel when there is fluid mucus.
Coccus Cacti with spasmodic coughing.
Kali Bich for yellow mucus.
Rumax or *Spongia* for older animals with heart problems.
Scilla with vomiting.

Collapse, stasis

Use *Carbo Veg.*

Conjunctivitis

Arg Nit, Pulsatilla, Hypericum and *Calendula* (diluted 1/40) can be given in water as an eye bath.

Constipation

Mark Elliott recommends:
Aesculus Hippocastanum typically to assist the case which is suffering a large, hard, dry stool with sharp fragments, such as bones, and is painful to pass.
Antimonium Crud for constipation alternating with diarrhoea.
Nux Vom use with frequent ineffectual urging, often following a dietary indiscretion.
Opium for constipation with absence of desire for stool. If passed the stool is of round, hard, black balls. Shy stool, appears and recedes.
Silicea when the stool is dry and passed with great difficulty, which often, when partially expelled, slips back in.

George MacLeod recommends:
Alumen is applicable when there is also sickness.
Bryonia is appropriate when there are hard dark stools.
Lycopodium should be given when there are liver or breathing difficulties as well.
Nat Mur is for general debilitation.
Nux Vom is for digestive problems generally.

Cystitis

There are several possibilities: *Cantharis, Urtica Urens, Uva Ursi* and *Causticum* in difficult cases.
Merc Cor may be appropriate for severe cases.

Diabetes

According to Francis Hunter *Syzygium Jumbul* can be a very effective remedy.

Diarrhoea, digestive problems and enteritis

The following can aid in diarrhoea: *Aconite, Arg Nit, Antimonium Crudum, Arsen Album, Dulcamara, Gelsemium, Merc Sol, Rhus Tox, Sulphur, Veratrum Album, Nat Sulph* and *Sepia.*
In severe cases or with haemorrhaging *China Officinalis* and *Croton Tiglium* should be given.
Morgan Gaertner may cure.
Nux Vomica has also been successful with my sick dogs.
Phosphorus should normally be given if there is vomiting and pain.
Camphora may be useful for enteritis caused by salmonella.
Aloes may help spluttery jelly-like diarrhoea.

Ears

Malandrium may help some forms of ear mites. Also *Calendula* diluted 1/20 in water.
Aconitum and *Hepar Sulph* are appropriate for inflammation of the middle ear. *Merc Sol* when the ear is sore and red inside. *Belladonna, Ferrum Phos, Merc Cor, Pulsatilla, Silicea, Tellurium* and *Rhus Tox* can also help with ear problems.

Epilepsy

Belladonna, Arnica, Cocculus, Nat Sulph, Opium, Stramonium and *Tarentula Hispanica* are the main remedies.

Eye conditions

Cineraria Maritima can be given diluted 1/10 in water.

Hippozaenium may help the tear-filled eyes.

Eye injuries Give *Ledum Palustre*.

Fever *Aconite*, fever and infection – *Belladonna, Dulcamara* can aid in cases of exposure. For E N fevers use *Ferrum Phos* and for septicaemia *Pyrogen 1M* may help.

Fleas *Sulphur* may make the animal less attractive to fleas and improve coat, nails and skin.

Gums and teeth *Calc Fluor* may be helpful for abscesses. *Fragaria* helps in dissolving tartar. *Merc Viv* is useful for gingivitis. *Hepar Sulph, Merc Sol* and *Silicea* may also be helpful.

Haemorrhaging If slow give *Crotalus Horr* and if fast *Ipecacuanha. Arnica* can be of use.

Infertility *Sepia* is particularly helpful to females and *Pulsatilla* is good for the ovaries.

Injuries For general injuries give *Arnica* or *Symphytum* (comfrey). *Hypericum* may help pain.

Laryngitis Give *Aconitum, Apis Mel, Rhus Tox,* or *Baryta Carb. Silicea* can be administered in extreme cases.

Lungs For fluid on the lung give *Apis Mel, Crataegus* or *Adonis Vert.*
If there is a respiratory problem *Spongia Tosta* can be of use.

Maternal instinct *Sepia Officinalis* may help with bitches that are not interested in their puppies.
Staphisagria will help those that ignore them after a difficult birth.

Miscarriages *Viburnum Opulis* or *Plumbum* should help in establishing a normal pregnancy.

Musculo-skeletal The major remedies are: *Arnica, Bryonia, Calc Carb, Causticum, Conium, Ledum Palustre, Pulsatilla, Rhus Tox* and *Rhuta Grav.*

Osteoporosis In the young *Calc Phos* is particularly good. *Calcarea Fluor* hardens bone. *Hecla Lava* and *Silicea* can also help.

Pancreatic problems George MacLeod recommends *Iris Vers, Atropinom, Chionanthus* and *Aconitum*; the pancreas nosode will be of use with associated remedies. *Morgan Bowel Nosode* should be used prior to introduction of the selected remedy.

Pleurisy	*Aconitum, Belladonna, Bryonia* or *Arsen Alb* are the appropriate remedies.
Pneumonia	*Aconitum, Bryonia, Arsen Iod,* or *Phosphorus* could be given.
Pregnancy	*Viburnum Opulis* in correct potency may benefit for the first few weeks and *Caulophyllum* in precise doses may help contractions if given at the end of the pregnancy. Overdosing can cause abortion. *Arnica* may help prevent haemorrhaging.
Respiratory problems	*Rumex Crispus* is useful in some instances.
Rhinitis	*Arsenicum Album, Pulsatilla* or *Kali Bich* are the main remedies.
Shock	*Aconite* and *Arnica* are the best remedies. *Bach's Rescue Remedy,* one or two drops on the tongue, is also excellent for shock, stress and travel nerves.
Sickness	For sea sickness give *Tabacum Tobacco.* For car sickness give *Cocculus* or *Petroleum.*
Sinusitis (With nasal discharge)	*Hepar Sulph, Silicea* or *Lemna Minor* may help.
Skin conditions	Give *Sulphur*. This is particularly good with mange, eczema and other skin problems. Other possible remedies are *Arsen Alb, Graphites, Hepar Sulph, Kali Phos, Allergens, Pulsatilla, Psorinum, Rhus Tox, Sepia, Silicea* and *Urtica Urens.*
Spleen problems	*Ceanothus* is the appropriate remedy.
Strokes	*Aconitum, Bufo, Arnica* or *Conium* are useful remedies.
Thrombosis	*Crotalus, Lachesis,* or *Vipera* should be given.
Tonsillitis	*Aconitum, Belladonna* or *Rhus Tox* may be beneficial. In chronic cases *Baryta Carb* and *Hepar Sulph* can be administered.
Urinary tract	The major remedies are: *Apis Mel, Berberis, Cantharis, Equisetum, Pulsatilla* and *Sepia.*
Warts	*Thuja Occidentalis* should help.
Wounds	Open wounds can benefit from *Calendula Officinalis* along with *Hypericum* also for nerve damage.

Calendula is also excellent when used as a cream after spaying. Puncture wounds, insect bites and eye injuries should be treated with *Ledum Palustre*. Septic wounds may benefit from *Chininum Sulphuricum*. *Echinacea* is also good for septic conditions. For fear and sudden infection give *Aconite* and when infected *Silicea*. The remedy for fractures is *Syphytum*. For lacerations give *Staphisagria* and for trauma use *Arnica*.

HOMOEOPATHY AND DISEASES

These are just a few of the homoeopathic remedies available for our dogs. For more detailed information on the appropriate remedy and dosage please consult a homoeopathic vet. Alternatively invest in George MacLeod's, Francis Hunter's, Dr Richard Pitcairn's, or Mark Elliott's homoeopathic books.

If you are a sceptic or question the value of homoeopathy the time to turn to it is when conventional medicine has failed and you have nothing to lose. Many, many times I have been amazed at the successes I have had using homoeopathy on my numerous dogs. It is definitely *not* mumbo jumbo and given the correct remedy it can work miracles when all other avenues have failed.

When administering pills the obvious thing is to try to hide the remedy in food, but if you don't succeed I suggest you use a pill popper, a syringe (if liquid) or crush the pill to a powder, put it in the fold of a small piece of paper and tip it down the throat. I find liquid remedies the best as they can be administered to any part of the mucous membranes and are absorbed at once. Homoeopathic remedies are available from the more enlightened pharmacies, health food shops and some pet stores. For more precise information you should consult your nearest homoeopathic vet, and most of the British homoeopathic vets are listed under the section Notable Names at the rear of the book.

TRUSTED TIPS

The following are a few useful tips which can improve the health of your dog with very little extra effort:

1. Do get your new puppy or dog inoculated whether conventionally or homoeopathically before you allow it to go outside and mix with other dogs, particularly if you live in a built-up area.

2. Vaccinations are an object of dispute. They can harm and they can kill. Make sure your animal is in optimum condition before vaccinating. Kipling, my Dobermann, was extremely ill after a booster vaccination and died prematurely at the age of six.

3. If you can, keep a patch in the garden to grow garlic and borage. The leaves are favourites with Little Dorrit and Roscoe. In the winter you can give cooked garlic and borage oil to keep your dog in optimum condition.

4. Do provide enough toys and chews for your puppy's 'mad moments'.

5. Do not overfeed. Overfeeding can cause diarrhoea in puppies, and obese dogs are unfit dogs. Any food that is left should always be removed and either thrown away or put in the refrigerator and kept for one more serving.

6. If your dog tumbles into oil you can remove it with a bath of washing-up liquid, taking care not to get it in the dog's eyes.

7. Sensitive dogs can be shampooed with gentle baby shampoos and Corpore Sano anti-parasite shampoo with chrysanthemum and citronella is also good for deterring fleas and ticks.

8. Try to give liver once or twice a week as it contains folic acid, but not too much as it can cause diarrhoea.

9. Fleas – *an adult flea can lay as many as 500 eggs in its lifetime.* One of Britain's top holistic veterinary experts, Timothy Couzens, recommended (in the April 1997 edition of *Pet Dogs*) the following treatments for trying to control the 'flea war':

   - Dried lavender, rosemary and sage placed in dishes around the house or in muslin bags inside your dog's bed to keep fleas at bay.

   - Lavender oil combed through your dog's coat as fleas won't like it.

   - A daily teaspoon of organic apple cider vinegar in your dog's water bowl. (This can also help in preventing intestinal worms.)

   - Vitamin Bs, as fleas don't like them. Add some brewer's yeast or a vitamin B complex to your dog's dinner.

10. I also advocate adding garlic to food as it may help to keep fleas at bay. It is also excellent for older dogs and is said to be good for the heart and circulation. A garlic clove is a healthy addition to food, but should not be given at the same time of day as vitamins and minerals. It is very strong and can diminish their efficacy.

11. You can buy herbal flea collars or you can make your own cotton collars with a piece of elastic and drops of eucalyptus oil or pennyroyal.

12. A walnut-sized piece of yellow rock sulphur in your dog's water bowl may help to deter fleas, ticks and worms.

13. For stings rub on raw garlic or onion.

14. For insect bites rub on lemon or garlic juice, or give the homoeopathic remedy *apis mel* or *urtica urens*.

15. *Silicea* is the homoeopathic remedy for removing splinters or thorns.

16. For inflamed eyes bathe with raw cucumber juice.

17. For canker of the ear mix one part lemon juice to three parts warm water or one or two drops of juniper essential oil diluted with a carrier oil.

18. For constipation give dried fruits: figs, dates, raisins, prunes, fresh fruits, bran and whole grain cereals.

19. Honey and ginger are good for travel sickness. The homoeopathic remedies are *tabacum, petroleum* or *cocculus indicus*.

20. Bach's Rescue Remedy is excellent for countering stress in a dog, it is also excellent for journeys. For an extremely nervous dog it often helps to transport the dog in a cage with a blanket over the top.

21. For hip dysplasia give cooked porridge oats and vitamins C and E.

22. *Sasparilla, urtica urens, merc cor* or *cantharis* may cure urinary infections.

23. Pregnant bitches are aided in whelping in their last two weeks of pregnancy by wild raspberry leaves.

24. Puppies whose mothers cannot feed them should be given fresh goat's milk, preferably unpasteurised. If there is a lactose intolerance, switch to cooked chicken breast and porridge as soon as possible.

25. Cottage cheese is the least fatty, while sheep's and goats' cheeses are more digestible.

26. For problems with anal glands try brewing linseed tea.

27. Before and after surgery give Chlorella Growth Factor or the Canine Care antioxidant to boost the immune system. The homoeopathic remedy *arnica* may also help.

28. For poisoning try giving salt water or vinegar and mustard, mixed two to one to induce vomiting. You could also give a tablespoon of bicarbonate of soda to a quarter of a cup of water, or the homoeopathic remedy *arsen alb*.

29. For arthritis give comfrey and try putting rock sulphur in the drinking water. Evening primrose oil is particularly good for aches and keeping everything supple. The homoeopathic remedies *ledum*, *rhus tox* or *ruta* are good for stiff joints.

30. If your dog has a persistent cough and lung problems which may be due to a faulty heart, Mark Elliott advocates his cactus crataegus remedy. Conventional drugs may be necessary. The homoeopathic remedy *rumex crispus* may help coughs.

31. If you are feeding inexpensive canned foods, give cod-liver oil and wheatgerm oil twice a week. I find that as a dog gets older its digestive system gets less robust and it needs purer, unadulterated food with vitamin and mineral supplements, oils, antioxidants and, sometimes, stomach enzymes as well. Techni-Cal, Hills, Eukanuba, Naturediet, Menu, Butcher's and Hi-Life are my preferred cans for dogs.

32. Do beware of canned foods containing unnamed preservatives, additives, colourants, caramels and genetically modified foods. Vitamin E is the best preservative. Ethoxiquin is used as a preservative and it is made from rubber. Manufacturers are not obliged to list the preservatives but if you write to them they will inform you. Semi-moist foods contain the most preservatives and the most sugars. Personally I prefer cans or dried biscuit for my dogs.

33. I think all-in-one biscuits are very good as tooth cleaners but I have my reservations about feeding them as a sole food, based on personal experience. If a dog eats dried food it needs to drink water in order not to dehydrate and ruin its kidneys and the water in your area may not be ideal even if filtered. The problem with most canned foods however are the 'by-products' and 'derivatives' which are an unknown quantity so try to choose cans with minimal derivatives and by-products and a high vitamin content. Even so, a lot of the vitamin content may be destroyed by the heat processing so a multi-mineral, vitamin supplement may be beneficial, and you can add kelp, wheatgerm, cooked oats, oatbran and vitamin E directly on to the food. It is a sad fact of life that the more expensive products are normally better than the cheap ones.

34. If you are feeding low quality foods, particularly in these days of chemicals and pesticides, in order to keep your dog's immune system healthy give canine vitamins and minerals, antioxidants and essential oils.

35. Ground egg shell sprinkled on to your dog's food is a good source of calcium (calcium carbonate) which will aid bone building. The best source is free-range eggs that have been cleaned thoroughly. Bonemeal containing phosphorus and calcium can also be added to meat diets as an extra source of calcium.

36. For skin problems witch hazel and calamine can be both calming and curative for non-nutritional skin conditions.

    Skin problems due to poor nutrition can be caused by an intolerance to dairy products or cheap foods. Vitamin E and a tiny amount of fish oil can help (never overdose on fish oils as too much vitamin A and D can be harmful). You can also give aloe vera internally. Sulphur is also very beneficial for skin conditions and is especially important when dealing with mange. It can be given both internally and externally. Rubbing fresh lemon juice directly on to mange-infected areas can be beneficial. If you want to make a good skin toner for dogs suffering from fleas or mange, bring 20 fl oz (570 ml) water to the boil – add 1 thinly sliced lemon – allow to steep overnight – sponge the liquid on to your dog and let it dry naturally. If the mange proves very stubborn Ivermectin from your vet may be the answer. The homoeopathic remedy for sore or broken skin is *calendula* and I used it very effectively and safely on Sophie's two young puppies. Vitamin E capsules and honey can also be rubbed directly on to the skin if there are bald patches and a raw food diet may also help. Tea tree oil and aloe vera are excellent for skin problems. For mild eczema, chop up an organic carrot. Put in a blender until perfectly smooth. Place on the infected area, bandage and leave for a couple of hours. Repeat as often as required. This treatment can also be used for minor wounds, sores or insect bites.

If your dog has very dry skin try curing it with a banana or avocado:

Peel a banana and mash it – add ¼ teaspoon of extra virgin olive oil – comb the mashed banana through the coat at the dry patch – allow to dry and rinse off with water.

Cut an avocado in half – remove the stone – scoop out the flesh and mash – rub the inside of the avocado skin on the dry patch and then comb the mashed avocado through the coat – let it dry before rinsing off with water.

37. If you want to stop a dog fight do not go into the mêlée with bare hands, the dogs will simply think you are a third dog come to join the battle and turn on you. The best way to separate two warring mutts is with a hose or a bucket of water. If neither is available a rug thrown over the assailant will immobilise the offender and sometimes a commanding loud vocal sound is sufficient. I have found that worming dogs invisibly affected by worms can make their personality more docile. Also feeding too much meat may encourage hyper-activity and irritability.

38. If your dog has a serious disease and the prognosis is said to be poor do *not* give up. Pure cooked foods, occasional liver and large doses of canine vitamins, minerals, antioxidants, essen-

tial oils and stomach enzymes can help and also sulphur or garlic which may deter parasites.

39. If your dog looks like getting kennel cough make sure it is kept warm, but that the room is well aired and not too hot.

40. For stressed rescue dogs Mark Elliott recommends the homoeopathic remedies: *nat mur* for grief and *calc phos* for disturbed puppies.

41. A small amount of chopped liquorice can help an incontinent dog. If your dog suffers from vomiting try adding a daily dose of fennel seeds to its diet. One teaspoon for a small dog, two teaspoons for a medium dog and three teaspoons for a large dog.

42. Always remember that if you do not have any herbs or alternative remedies to hand, a teaspoon of salt dissolved in a pint of hot water and cooled slightly can be used to bathe any kind of sore, wound or infection.

43. If you have to have your dog put down please ask for a premed to make it woozy before the lethal injection. That way it is unaware when the needle goes in, is not distressed and passes away serenely.

44. Do not be surprised at your own grief over the death of your dog. It will have been a family member and part of your life, hopefully, for several years. I find I need to talk to other caring dog owners who understand the need to grieve and appreciate notes of condolence. I too send cards of sympathy when friends' animals die. There is no doubt the loss of a pet hurts and the lack of their presence cannot be dismissed lightly. The homoeopathic remedy ignatia can be given to both humans and animals who are grieving.

ALEXANDRA'S FIRST AID BOX

- A list of vets' names and telephone numbers.

- A homoeopathic first aid kit. Francis Hunter recommends the following as a starter kit: *aconite, apis mel, arnica, arsen alb, bryonia, cantharis, carbo veg, chamomilla, cocculus, colocynthus, euphrasia, gelsemium, hepar sulph, hypericum, merc cor, merc sol, nux vomica, pulsatilla, rhus tox, scutellaria, silicea, sulphur, symphytum* and *urtica*.

- Bioforce Echinacea.

- Bach's Rescue Remedy.

- Canine multi-vitamin and mineral, antioxidant and essential oils, vitamin C crystals, vitamin B complex, cod-liver oil, bonemeal tablets, desiccated liver tablets, acidophilus powder (stomach enzymes), organic garlic capsules.

- Pill popper, pill crusher, syringe (minus the needle) for administering liquids, eye droppers, Vaseline, tweezers, blanket, nail clippers, scissors.

- Rock sulphur for water bowls or sulphur tablets.

- Leo ear cleaner for ear mites.

- Scissors, rectal thermometer.

- Aerated bandages.
- Plastic lampshade with collar to prevent dog from getting at sores or stitches.
- Old socks to put over bandages for dogs which are bandage destroyers.
- Dog handbooks! See bibliography at the end of book.
- Euphrasia eye wash.
- Muzzle and halti.
- *Calendula, arnica* and *hypericum* creams.
- Tea tree ointment.
- Sulphur and Corpore Sano anti-parasite shampoos.
- Flea comb, collars and spray.
- Wormer tablets/powders for roundworm and tapeworm.

IF YOU HAVE . . .

- If you have an allergy to dogs, have you ever thought of getting a Poodle, a Mexican Hairless or Chinese Crested as they have a coat which may be easier to tolerate? They all have delightful, affectionate dispositions and are fun. However, you may want to check if your allergies are food related. I used to have chronic hay fever until I gave up dairy products and ate only organic, old-fashioned non-GM wheat. I no longer have a problem. Also, do you ever worm yourself with a family, over-the-counter wormer? This may improve your health.

- If you have a new baby be careful about giving your dog access to it alone. Children under the age of three should not, as a general rule, be left unsupervised with animals.

- If you have to move house be careful not to upset your dog as this is a time when a dog may escape the commotion of the removal men and disappear. The best thing is to keep them locked in a room (possibly the bathroom where there is no furniture) until you are ready to transfer them to their new abode. Bach's Flower Remedy walnut can help dogs to cope with changes.

- If you have a dog that has smelly faeces try putting it on a pure diet. Putting a walnut-sized piece of sulphur in their water may also help.

- If you have a dog that is showing signs of unusual aggression for no obvious reason, it could indicate that your pet is suffering from physical pain such as arthritis.

- If you have a dog that chews its paws or mutilates itself, this may be due to lack of exercise, boredom, stress or incorrect feeding.

- If you have a dog that appears short of breath, or coughs, it could mean a heart problem.

- If you have a dog that suddenly starts to drink a large amount of water and urinates frequently, this could mean the onset of diabetes or kidney disease.

- If you have a dog whose mouth and the conjunctiva of its eyes look pale, it could be a sign that your pet is suffering from anaemia; if they look yellow then it could be suffering from liver problems.

- If you have a dog that produces white faeces, do not be alarmed, this could be due to eating bones.

- If you have a dog that smells bad overall, this could mean an ear infection, gum, kidney or skin problem.

- If you have a dog that starts chewing its paws, it may have a problem with anal glands.

WHAT'S IN

- For your dog's safety whenever it is out be sure it is wearing a collar with a name-tag, including your address and/or telephone number in case it goes missing.

- Brush your dog's coat regularly. Check for any skin problems and examine ears, eyes, paws etc.

- Regularly wash your dog's bed and keep its covers aired and vacuum clean regularly. This will prevent flea eggs from hatching.

- Feed your dog its food at room temperature and at the same times each day – preferably with the main meal in the morning.

- Have fresh drinking water available at all times and change daily. Boil or filter the water for cleanliness.

- Use stainless steel or ceramic dog bowls – plastic ones may affect the food or water and consequently your dog's health.

- For a truly healthy dog, one hour's walk every day would not go amiss.

- Take a pooper scooper with you on walks and train your dog to use the gutter or side of paths. You can be fined if your dog fouls the footpath or pavement.

- If your dog is wet after a walk, dry it well or it may get a chill.

- When travelling in the car with a dog, make sure there is enough ventilation. Stop every hour or two to give your dog water and exercise.

- Do use an extension lead or muzzle for unpredictable, eccentric dogs. I have found the best muzzles are the soft plastic ones by Roger Mugford.

- If you have a spiteful dog, consult your vet about castration as it can be helpful.

- Do try to give a home to a rescue dog. Hundreds of unwanted pets are put down every day.

- To train a dog to use a dog flap, putting food on the other side is often the answer.

- If you purchase cans of dog food, whenever possible recycle the cans.

- You can cut a dog's nails that get too long, but this should be done under expert supervision with proper nail clippers and be sure not to cut the pink quick as the nail will bleed profusely and be very painful. If you have any doubts ask your vet to cut the nails for you.

- If you are out at work all day do get two dogs to keep each other company.

- If your dog goes missing place advertisements in the local paper, in all the local shops, and on trees and inform the police, the local RSPCA, vets and animal centres. The best idea with modern technology is to get your vet to tattoo the ear or microchip the dog's identity into its neck. That way its ownership can never be in dispute and it can always be traced.

- Most important of all do get your dog spayed or neutered.

- The ideal dog for city dwellers are King Charles Spaniels, Pugs or

Maltese Terriers as they don't need so much exercise.

- If there's a stray mutt in your area please contact your local RSPCA centre or do a spot of dog rescue yourself.
- If you have occasion to use bandages, use the aerated varieties so the air can get to the wound. Alternatively a plastic lampshade around the dog's head may be the answer, as the wound can be left open to the air without the dog getting at it.

WHAT'S OUT

- Do not be alarmed if your new dog does not eat at first, it is quite a common phenomenon. If you get really anxious try titbits like fresh chicken, chopped beef with dog biscuits or a little liver.

- Never overfeed your dog.

- Don't put your dog's bed in a damp area or where there is a draught. It is easy to make a slatted wood base to raise the bed off the floor – this also airs the bed well.

- Don't use added salt or sugar, white bread or white rice when cooking for your dog.

- Don't feed a dog while you are eating, despite the pleading eyes.

- Avoid giving an adult-dog milk – it may have a lactose intolerance.

- Avoid feeding the following foods: chocolate (it can be poisonous to dogs), bacon, ham, pork, parsnips and peanuts because they may cause an allergic reaction or digestive problems. Some dogs are also known to have a wheat allergy. My dogs have a particular allergy to genetically modified wheat.

- If your new dog is sick upon arrival this is probably due to stress. If the sickness continues starve the dog for twenty-four hours and then give a diet of fresh chicken or rabbit and rice. If the dog has come from an unknown source the sickness may be due to negligence and lack of worming. The wormer Panacur treats tapeworm and roundworm for dogs and also giardia in weaned puppies.

- Smoked meats and smoked fish should be given very rarely because of the salt content.

- If you are introducing a new puppy to an old dog do not leave them unattended until you are convinced they are friends.

- *Never* leave a dog in a car without some form of ventilation. It is particularly important in the summer months to be vigilant as your dog will die in a hot car with inadequate ventilation.

- Dogs should never be allowed to hang their heads out of a moving vehicle – something could fly into their eyes and cause injury.

- Don't travel with a dog loose at any time. It can easily jump out of an open window or door, it can also cause accidents. There are many good dog cages and harnesses for cars available.

- Don't leave a dog chained for hours at a time – it can make them aggressive.

- Don't get a large dog if you are not going to walk it for at least one hour a day.

- Don't leave a puppy or young dog alone with the Christmas tree. Kipling dragged our Christmas tree around the room in order to reach all the chocolate ornaments.

- Be very wary of using metal choke chains as they may cause neck problems in later years.

A-Z OF HEALTHY HINTS

'One dog's food is another dog's poison.'

Alexandra Bastedo

adapted from 'One man's food is another man's poison.'

Hippocrates

The following health remedies are based on nutrition and herbs. For easy reference I have included some of the homoeopathic remedies again.

A is For:

ABSCESSES

To have less chance of abscesses due to fights the animals should be neutered. Sulphur may also help.
Homoeopathically: *Lachesis muta* should be given immediately as a single dose for preventative measures and *silicea* should be given when the abscess is fully formed. *Streptococcus* and *hepar sulph* are also important remedies.
Herbally: Echinacea helps to purify and boost the immune system and I have had success with putting honey and chlorella powder poultices on abscesses.

ACUPUNCTURE

Acupuncture can have remarkable results with slipped discs, arthritis, epilepsy and many other problems. I took Dorrit, screaming in pain to our vet, Peter Brown, and after acupuncture there was nothing wrong with her.

ANAEMIA

Anaemia can be caused by incorrect nutrition. If it is caused by worms or fleas the appropriate remedy should be used. My preferred veterinary wormers are Endorid (for roundworm) and Drontal (for tapeworm) and Panacur for roundworm and tapeworm in dogs. Anaemia predominantly results from lack of iron and B vitamins which can be helped by adding a little lamb or chicken liver twice a week plus broccoli, oats, kelp, vitamin C powder (up to 1000 milligrams per day for a large dog), a vitamin B complex and canine vitamins and minerals and antioxidants. I also use Feroglobin, which is a liquid iron and vitamin supplement. For a dog on a vegetarian diet alfalfa, raspberry leaf and comfrey should also be given.
Homoeopathically: *China officinalis* could be given and *ferrum metallicum* where there is an iron deficiency and *cinchona* can supplement other remedies when there is weakness and lethargy due

to loss of body fluid. (Where there are accompanying liver problems or jaundice George MacLeod recommends the homoeopathic remedies: *crotalus horr* and *lachesis*.)
Herbally: Echinacea is an excellent immune system booster. It should not be used all the time as it works better when given in fortnightly (daily) bursts.

ANTIOXIDANTS

Canine Care antioxidants are designed to be a real weapon in the fight against damage to the body by pollutants, chemicals in food, stress and age deterioration. Antioxidants may help in the treatment of, among others, allergies, arthritis, cancer, heart disease, cataracts, liver disease, skin problems and viral infections. The antioxidant activity is formed by a combination of vitamins A, C, E, selenium and herbs including echinacea for its immune system boosting capabilities.

ANXIETY

First try to work out the cause of the anxiety and try to rectify the situation.
Homoeopathically: *Aconite, arsen alb, nux vom* and *arg nit* can help calm down a nervous animal. Anxiety when moving house is often alleviated by the homoeopathic remedies *capsicum* 6c or phosphorus acid 6c four times daily for seven to ten days. Other possible remedies for anxiety including fear and aggression are: *ignatia, pulsatilla, anacardium, belladonna, gelsemium, lachesis, hyoscyamus, staphisagria* and *stramonium*.
Herbally: Agrimony, valerian, skullcap and aspen can be beneficial. My vet advocates many of the Bach Flower Remedies, and Bach's Rescue Remedy is excellent for fearful travellers. The Bach Flower Remedy honeysuckle may also be helpful.

ARTHRITIS

Overweight dogs should be put on a diet immediately to lose weight. Extra calcium or bonemeal should be added to food and greenleaf, garlic and seaweed tablets could help. Oils such as evening primrose oil, vitamin E daily and a little cod-liver oil twice a week along with vitamin C should be beneficial. (It is important never to overdose cod-liver oil so a quarter of a teaspoon is suffi-

cient for a small dog.) Nutritionally, vitamin C, A and D and E supplements are the most beneficial and collagen supplements could be useful. In severe cases the drug vivitonin can help, but consult your vet first.
Homoeopathically: *Rhus tox* is the most commonly used remedy and *bryonia* and *pulsatilla* may be of use. For older dogs try *arnica. Sulphur* is also thought to help. *Ledum palustre* or *lac caninum* may be good for arthritic joints.
Herbally: Alfalfa and garlic may help.

B is For:

BAD BREATH

Bad breath may mean bad teeth which should be extracted by the vet. The condition may have been caused by too much sugar in some commercial foods. Dog biscuits, a marrow bone or raw vegetables can make good tooth cleaners or – a tooth brush! If you suspect the problem is intestinal, a fast is advised, followed by a fish and rice diet until the problem has gone. Charcoal biscuits in moderation can also help and I would advise a change of commercial dog food to Naturediet, Butcher's, Menu, Eukanuba, Techni-Cal, Hills, Nutro or James Wellbeloved.
Homoeopathically: *Calc fluor* is good for tooth and gum disorders. *Morgan Gaertner* can help when halitosis is due to stomach problems. *Nux vomica* or *rhus tox* are useful.
Herbally: Garlic and alfalfa in food can work.

BELLIGERENCE

A wormy dog can be aggressive so de-worm regularly. Also cut back on protein – turkey is the most calming meat.
Homoeopathically: *Hyoscyamus* and *staphisagria* are two of the best remedies for aggressive, territorial dogs.
Herbally: The most calming herbs are valerian and skullcap. Bach's Rescue Remedy can be given to the victim of the intimidation.

BITCH

If you are contemplating mating your bitch, remember all the unwanted canines in the world and also that rearing puppies properly is more expensive than actually investing in a spaying operation. The poor pregnant bitches that end up in rescue centres are normally in a dreadful state – flea-ridden, undernourished and emaciated. They give birth to wormy, undersized puppies often with abnormalities or with such a poor immune system that they lose the fight for survival. What a depressing business it is too.

So if you insist on breeding your bitch she should be fed with the very best of pure foods particularly high in protein. Crushed egg shell or a calcium supplement is most important as are vitamin C (500–1000 mg), a B complex (30 mg), vitamin E (50–100 iu), kelp and a canine multi-mineral which should be given daily. One teaspoon of extra virgin olive oil should be added to food and a quarter of a teaspoon of cod-liver oil should be given three times a week. Chicken or lambs' liver should also be cooked twice a week.

Watch out for a condition called *eclampsia* at the end of or after pregnancy which occurs because of a lack of calcium. The puppies take a great deal of calcium from their mother's body. Usually the symptoms are violent trembling, but there may also be a high fever accompanied by loss of appetite. To prevent this you should give the pregnant bitch calcium carbonate or powdered egg shell or bonemeal early in pregnancy.

Homoeopathically: *Viburnum* can be useful in early pregnancy to avoid miscarrying. If there is haemorrhaging give either *arnica* or *ipecac*. For calcium deficiency/depletion you can give *belladonna* 6c every fifteen minutes but you would be advised to see a veterinarian as soon as possible for calcium injections to prevent eclampsia.

BURNS

Give vitamin B (in complex form) C, E, fish oils (A and D) and zinc. Bach's Rescue Remedy or a couple of drops of brandy in half a teaspoon of liquid honey can be helpful if the dog is in shock.

Homoeopathically: Externally *urtica urens* diluted in water can be put on a bandage and kept damp on the affected area or *calendula* can be smoothed on. The homoeopathic remedy *cantharis* can be given.

C is For:

CANCER

The word cancer inspires fear in every heart. However, there are changes in diet and vitamin supplements that can help and, in some cases, even prolong life. Early diagnosis is most important so do keep an eye out for subtle changes in your dog. On no account should the animal be given commercial dog foods full of colourants, additives, sugars, preservatives and chemicals. Feed your dog free-range, good, raw or cooked meats (chicken, rabbit, turkey, pheasant and lamb), cooked mackerel, sardines, herring and tuna with raw organic vegetables and herbs (except parsnips, celery and parsley). If you prefer to cook the vegetables, lightly steam them to preserve their goodness. The most important anti-cancer vitamin is C in large doses. Selenium is the most effective mineral, in combination with vitamins A, C and E. Organic garlic, echinacea, essiac and herbal remedies are good immune system boosters for all forms of cancer. Juliette de Bairacli Levy recommends turnip, aloe vera and grape juice as well. The other extremely important factor for the animal is no stress so see if you can give your pet a calm but not too sedentary life as exercise can also be beneficial because cancer hates oxygen, so plenty of walks in the fresh air are recommended.

CATARACTS

Cataracts may be related to diabetes so cut back on any fatty or sweet treats and replace them with raw carrots and apples. Aloe vera juice, blackcurrant oil, beta carotene and vitamin E all help maintain healthy eyes.

COCCIDIOSIS

Coccidiosis is a disease caused by an intestinal parasite called isospora or by eimeria. There are four types of isospora parasites which affect dogs and are commonly diagnosed in puppies less than one year old. Although species of isospora are found in mature animals, they rarely cause serious problems and most infections will be resolved through self immunisation. The symptoms of coccidiosis are similar to those seen in puppies with giardiasis, namely: diarrhoea, dehydration, lethargy, abdominal tenderness and anorexia. A vet should be consulted immediately if you see any sign of these symptoms as the disease can easily be cured if treated early in young puppies. Isospora is diagnosed by examining the dogs' faeces microscopically. Many dogs will have the isospora parasite but not show any clinical signs of illness and live quite normally. However, they will shed the disease in their faeces and if the faeces are not removed the disease can be spread to other susceptible canines. It is very important to clean thoroughly and disinfect the areas where your dog has been unwell. It is only the young, weak and immuno-compromised animals that are at risk, as healthy adults do not seem to develop the disease. Isospora is most commonly seen in kennels and multiple dog households.

COLDS

At the onset of sneezing my dogs are the recipients of vitamin C (powder, pills or capsules) and zinc in particular, also Canine Care multi-vitamin-multi-minerals and antioxidants to boost the immune system. Sometimes I put echinacea drops diluted with water, in a syringe, and administer that also. I also put some Olbas Oil on the edge of their beds or a little eucalyptus oil. Tiger balm at a safe distance can also help to clear nasal passages. However, none of these oils should be put right next to the nose. You can also put your dog in the bathroom when you are having a hot bath as the steam can help congestion.
Homoeopathically: *Bryonia* is good for chest infections and many kinds of cough.

CONSTIPATION

Constipation can be due to nerves or more usually to incorrect feeding. Cook pure foods and add oat bran, organic garlic and a little extra virgin olive oil. Powdered stomach enzymes can also be helpful in correcting the balance of different floras in the gut. Organic raw meat and raw green vegetables and fresh fruit given on a regular basis should solve the problem. Raw rabbit and a touch of raw, grated broccoli would be a good start to get things moving. Oils are immediately helpful and on a regular basis oat bran should be added to your dog's meal. If this doesn't resolve the problem there could be an obstruction and a vet needs to be consulted. Useful supplements are: rhubarb tablets, vitamins E and C,

zinc and wheatgerm oil. A piece of rock sulphur in the water may also help.
Homoeopathically: *Aesculus hippocastanum, nux vom, opium, plumbum* and *silicea* are just some of the remedies that may be helpful. George MacLeod recommends *alumen* where there is also sickness, *bryonia* for dark hard stools and *nat mur* for general debilitation. *Nux vom* can be given for general digestive problems.

COUGHS

Vitamin C is most important; at the first cough or sneeze I always give my dogs between 500 and 1000 mg a day depending on the size of the dog. Vitamins A and D or fish oil should be given twice weekly (always be careful not to overdose A and D). Vitamin E works at its optimum level when combined with fish oil and selenium and zinc are also excellent immune system boosters.
Homoeopathically: *Bryonia* or *rumex crispus* may help.
Herbally: The best herbs for coughs are St John's Wort, echinacea and peppermint.

D is For:

DEATH

If death comes naturally *arsenicum album* can aid the animal's passage by calming it down. Tim Couzens recommends *aconite* when there is extreme agitation and restlessness. He says a few doses of *aconite* given at timely intervals can make a vast difference. Choosing euthanasia can be very difficult and personally I find picking that moment agonising, but often necessary. I believe that quality of life is all, and that if you can offer a way out to a pet that is suffering with no hope of recovery, then you should take it. This is not for three-legged dogs who often live minus one limb very happily for years but for fatally ill dogs that are in distress. However, I do believe in asking for a pre-med shot so that the animal is already asleep and not upset by the lethal injection. If you choose to let your dog die naturally you should not forcefeed it, just give it water and keep it quiet and warm. Dr Richard Pitcairn also recommends *arsenicum album* 30c for 90 per cent of dying animals. He also suggests *pulsatilla* 30c for an animal that is complaining and calling out or wanting to be held. A vet should be called to animals who are in agony, extremely agitated and screaming out in pain; but if he or she is a long time coming *tarentula cubensis* 30c is a useful remedy to give. If you are taking your dog to the vet Bach's Rescue Remedy can also calm the animal down.

DIABETES

Diabetic dogs need to be kept on a very strict non-sugar diet which immediately eliminates a number of commercial dog foods that have added sugar (often called caramels) and preservatives. If you don't know, you can always call the pet food manufacturer (see Appropriate Addresses) and ask them. However, to be absolutely sure there is no sugar in the food it is obviously better to indulge in home-cooking. The dog should have two light meals a day, preferably at the same time every day to stabilise the blood sugar levels. Protein should only be from beans and vegetables and a little lean meat or fish. Chromium is the best mineral to reduce blood sugar and brown rice, oats, nuts and seeds are rich in the necessary vitamin Bs. A limited amount of fruit should be given and extra vitamin C can be added to the diet, along with vitamin E and beta-carotene which may help deteriorating eyesight. Another helpful mineral is zinc and a herbal tea made with dandelion root can be given along with seaweed and garlic tablets. Also be sure to worm regularly and give sulphur as parasites and worms may exacerbate diabetes.
Homoeopathically: Dr Richard Pitcairn recommends *natrum muriaticum* 6x and Francis Hunter particularly advocates *syzigium jambolanum.* The suggested potency of 3x of the latter can be given three times daily and can actually help to reduce the amount of insulin given and in some mild cases it may replace the insulin altogether.
Herbally: Dandelion, seaweed and organic garlic are beneficial.

DIARRHOEA

This can be caused by a worm infestation, allergies, bacteria, viruses and parasites from infected areas or from contaminated food or water. The most important thing is to fast the animal for twenty-four hours but to make sure the animal is drinking pure water to avoid dehydration you could give lukewarm bottled water and honey. After that you can give a little live goats' yoghurt or stomach enzymes with a little white rice and free-range breast of chicken or fish until the dog is back to normal. Beware of giving milk as a lactose intolerance may actually contribute to the problem. Give only boiled or bottled water in case there is a change in your water supply. Also remove any flea collars and stop using flea products while the condition remains.

Homoeopathically: There are a number of remedies which can help. Apart from the remedies already mentioned in the homoeopathic section, Pitcairn suggests *podophyllum* 6c for typical diarrhoea and *mercurius corrosivus* 6c for dysentery often with straining and bloody stools. *Arsenicum album* 6c should be given after bad meat and *natrum muriaticum* 6x for longer lasting diarrhoea particularly when the dog sits hunched up on all fours after eating. *Pulsatilla* 6c may be given when dogs have binged or eaten food that is too rich for them.

Herbally: Slippery elm powder and roasted carob powder should be given. Children's kaolin may also correct the problem, but if it persists a vet should be consulted.

E is For:

EAR MITES

A Dr Pitcairn solution which works very well is three quarters of an ounce of almond oil, a quarter of an ounce of olive oil mixed with 400 iu of vitamin E (at body temperature). This should be massaged in the ear canal and excess oil should be removed gently with a cotton bud. The treatment should be given on alternate days over a six-day period. After three days he then advises a herbal infusion of rumex crispus every three days for three to four weeks. A sulphur or Corpore Sano anti-parasite shampoo may also be a good idea if you suspect the mites are outside the ear as well.

Pat McKay in her book *Reigning Cats and Dogs* recommends cleaning the ear with a solution which is 50 per cent witch hazel and 50 per cent water.

Homoeopathically: *Malandrium* may help ear mites and calendula diluted 1/10 in water. *Aconitum* and *hepar sulph* are good for inflammation of the middle ear, and *merc cor* or *rhus tox* should be given in the case of severe ear infection.

EPILEPSY AND FITS

Epilepsy is more common in dogs than cats. The most likely cause is a head injury or it may be inherited. Some vets now suspect vaccination. Mark Elliott and Dr Bruce Fogle, the Canadian/British vet, say the latest veterinary thinking is that vaccinations may be only necessary every three years. They should *never* be given if an illness is already suspected. This does present a problem with dog kennels, as legislation at present demands that dogs boarded there have annual vaccinations. Always seek veterinary advice. My Poodle, Noddy, had fits as a puppy. We were advised to lock him in a dark cupboard until they passed so that he did himself a minimum amount of injury. Diet is important in epilepsy and a hypoallergenic diet should be followed as colourants or allergies may trigger a fit. Only the purest foods like chicken and rice should be given, alternated with vegetables. A vitamin B complex – which is excellent for nerves – and vitamin C and zinc will also help. My Golden Retriever, Ben, developed a large lump on his head and started to have fits in his ninth year. We sought veterinary advice but as it proved to be a tumour and eventually the fits became intolerable for him, we had to have him put down. On the occasions when I have had to have my dogs put to sleep I have always fed them their favourite treats. That way they hardly notice the needle going in and pass away serenely.

Homoeopathically: *Belladonna* and *stramonium* are probably the first remedies to try particularly when the animals have dilated pupils and try to escape from their surroundings. For chronic persistent cases *ignatia* may be of benefit. George MacLeod recommends *cocculus* 6c as a remedy which can be used long term and may prevent seizures. He also suggests *nat sulph, opium* and *tarentula hispanica.*

Herbally: Skullcap and valerian are calming remedies for shattered nerves and Bach's Rescue Remedy can also help bring an animal round and calm its fear.

ESSENTIAL OILS

Essential fatty acids are increasingly being recognised as an important part of a dog's diet. They are essential for cell membranes and cell function throughout the body. Omega-3 essential fatty acids have beneficial effects on cardiovascular function, arthritis and other inflammatory conditions including eczema, dry skin or poor coat, mental deterioration and nerve problems. Omega-6 (borage oil) can help skin conditions, hair loss, fatigue, anaemia, kidney degeneration, liver problems and arthritis. When spirulina or chlorella are added to the oils they help to boost the immune system and detoxify the liver, blood and bowels from chemicals and heavy metals.

EYES

As a general cleanser a quarter of a teaspoon of salt in a quarter of a pint of bottled water is an easily made solution. For a herbal eyedrop infusion Diane Stein recommends cineraria, rue, sage tea or celandine and the floral essences crab apple, camphor or hawthorn for cleansing. Cucumber juice is also very soothing for sore eyes.

If there are cataracts this condition can be due to nutritional deficiencies, in particular a lack of vitamin C, the B complex, vitamins A, D and E, selenium and zinc.

Richard Pitcairn particularly advocates putting a drop of eucalyptus honey in eyes with cataracts twice a day for several weeks and reports that this procedure has resulted in cataract reductions and cures.

Homoeopathically: *Calc fluor* or *natrum mur* 30c may help with recently formed cataracts and *silicea* 200c is useful with established cataracts. *Ledum palustre* or *symphytum* 30c should be used when there are eye injuries and *euphrasia officinalis* is good when there are scratches or superficial cuts.

F is For:

FEAR

Homoeopathically: There are several remedies: *aconite, arnica, argentum nitricum, arsenicum album, gelsemium, ignatia, nux vomica, phosphorus, pulsatilla, staphisagria* and *stramonium.*

Aconite is recommended for dogs whose fear turns to anger and may be due to pain. *Argentum nitricum* and *arsenicum album* are good for dogs who have a restless manner and seem mentally rather anxious. *Gelsemium* is a useful remedy for very timid dogs who are sometimes paralysed with fear and then hide away at any disturbance. *Ignatia* should be given when there is worry over the death of a fellow dog or owner and when the dog has suffered a particularly traumatic experience. *Nux vomica* is appropriate for very nervous dogs who often hate being handled but will fight aggressively if cornered. *Pulsatilla* is for shy, gentle dogs, usually female who like the protection of human company. *Stramonium* and *arnica* should be given if a dog is distressed and unusually anxious about being handled, perhaps after a fright or an accident.

FIGHTING

Neutering can calm a dog. I also suggest worming regularly as it seems to calm dogs down and cut back on red meat if you are feeding your dog a high protein diet. Also check the small print on cans if feeding commercial food because they often contain colourants, additives and sugars which may be a cause of hyperactivity.
Homoeopathically: *Hyoscyamus* and *anacardium* may help.
Herbally: Skullcap and valerian are the remedies for calming down animals.

FLEAS

Fleas are an on-going battle. One doesn't want to be so heavy-handed with chemicals that the immune system is impaired but at the same time one does not want the flea to take over and create an infestation as that too will cause disease. I do not believe in giving chemicals internally but garlic and sulphur can be effective flea deterrents. The sugars in commercial pet foods may also make an animal more attractive to fleas and they are particularly vulnerable if they have a weak immune system. It is therefore very important to feed pure foods – whether cooked or commercial – and to supplement with a good canine multi-vitamin-mineral and antioxidants. The flea cycle can also create worms so de-worm regularly.

The main anti-flea herbs are eucalyptus, citronella, cedar, rosemary and fennel which can be pulverised and made into a flea powder. You can also make good herbal collars which are made from herbal oils. A good anti-parasite shampoo and tonic is Corpore Sano. Juliette de Bairacli Levy also recommends her lemon

skin tonic which is made by putting a sliced lemon into almost boiling water. It should be left to cool overnight and then put on the coat of the dog in question. It can be used on a daily basis as it is harmless. A flea comb is the other important piece of equipment as it picks up fleas as it moves through the hair and these can then be drowned in hot water with washing-up liquid added to it or popped between two thumb nails. If things cannot be controlled herbally then use a chemical spray or spot very sparingly and be on the alert for side-effects and do *NOT* overdose on any account. Just as important as the products is regular vacuuming and washing of bedding – which should be picked up carefully so nothing falls out – to get rid of flea dirt and eggs. See section on Trusted Tips for more ideas on controlling fleas.
Homoeopathically: *Urtica* can be given if there is an allergy to flea collars.

G is For:

GASTRITIS

Dogs are not as fussy as cats when it comes to eating, and can get gastric problems by consuming the wrong foods. These can be things they have scavenged or even a sharp object which has been eaten accidentally. Normally such objects need to be removed surgically and a delay can prove fatal. Food allergies are frequently a problem and I find that as a dog gets older it begins to show food intolerances. A fast of twenty-four hours is often beneficial followed by a complete change in diet to home-cooked foods such as lamb, chicken, pheasant, rabbit, turkey or pulses and rice, millet and grains. Stick to one type of meat and rice for at least ten days. With gastritis, stomach enzymes can also be helpful and give liquid vitamins if the animal is severely run-down and needs its immune system building up. Worms can also bring on vomiting and diarrhoea so your dog should also be checked for these and given either a wormer for roundworms (more common) or tapeworms (less common but very possible). Intestinal parasites could also be the cause and should be investigated by your vet who may have to treat the dog with prescribed drugs.
Homoeopathically: The nosode, *Gaertner-Bach* is suggested by

George MacLeod for chronic gastro-enteritis where there is a tendancy for the animal to become infested with worms. Associated remedies are *phosphorous* and *silicea*. The nosode *Morgan-Bach* may also help. Other remedies are: *nux vomica* for serious cases accompanied by thirst; *ipecac* for frequent sickness; *phosphorus* if there is vomiting with pain; *camphora* if the cause is salmonella; *arsenicum album* when the food is questionable; *pulsatilla* should be given when your pet is wanting your attention and drinks in an unfamiliar way; *hypericum* is useful when there is pain.
Herbally: Slippery elm, milk thistle, dandelion, peppermint and camomile are good digestive herbs.

GRIEF

Can dogs grieve? The answer is yes, they definitely can. Little Dorrit was very stressed and sad after her mother Daisy died. She was so used to doing everything with her and felt lonely even though we still had Roscoe the black Dobermann. Vitamin B2 is said to aid depression and can be effective in humans as well.
Homoeopathically: *Ignatia* is the main remedy for grief. *Nat mur* can be given after *ignatia*, particularly if the animal seems to want to be left alone. *Nux vom* is also possible for a dog that does not want to be handled; however, if the reverse is true and your pet craves attention, *pulsatilla* may be more appropriate. *Staphisagria* is good for grief when it is accompanied by symptoms such as hair loss. *Aurum* is appropriate when there is a deep depression and *causticum* works well when the animal appears to age after losing a companion (either animal or human) that has probably had a worrying illness over a long period. St. John's Wort (*hypericum*) can help to relieve depression.
Herbally: Camomile, skullcap and valerian are very calming. Honeysuckle or Star of Bethlehem may be given to animals when they have lost their owner or fellow dog. Olive can be helpful when the worry has been long-standing.

H is For:

HEALING

Dogs can respond very well to the laying on of hands by a genuine healer. A troubled or nervous dog can often become so calm under a healer's hands that it actually falls asleep. If an animal is fatally ill a healer can also be a very beneficial soothing presence.

HEART

Heart problems are fairly common in older dogs. There are excellent conventional veterinary drugs but there are also a number of things that can be done at home. The first thing is to make the animal lose any unnecessary weight by a) putting it on a sugar- and salt-free diet and cutting out 'treats' and b) trying to stop it being a couch potato by encouraging it to exercise a little more, whether with toys inside the home or with more time spent outside.

I always blamed myself for my Dobermann Sophie's heart condition as she had been fed far too many titbits, and was definitely too fat, which put a strain on her heart. From then on she had small portions of egg, tofu, poultry, rabbit, fish and rice twice daily and I would only feed her the original Denes cans, which they assured me did not contain salt.

Nutritionally, vitamins E, A and D are very important and also chromium, selenium, zinc and a B complex vitamin. An all-in-one canine multi-vitamin-multi-mineral would be a minimum requirement along with garlic and greenleaf tablets and in an older dog I would definitely boost the vitamin C daily intake to 500 mg. If the dog is taking heart tablets it may need to take extra potassium which could be depleted by the drugs. Omega-3 fatty acids are essential for a heart condition and can be found in mackerel, herring, sardine or tuna or alternatively you can give it in capsule form. If you need to add bulk to the meals you can add oatbran, wheatgerm and vegetables.

Homoeopathically: *Spongia tosta* may be useful, particularly when there is a cough. *Calc fluor* is good for a weakened heart muscle. *Crataegus oxycantha* may help if there is fluid retention.

Herbally: Juliette de Bairacli Levy makes a rosemary and honey tea for dogs with heart problems. Skullcap is calming and alfalfa helps with blood pressure while dandelion acts as a diuretic.

HYGIENE

Dogs are clean animals but in a domestic situation they need a bit of help. You will need to keep their bedding clean on a regular basis to get rid of flea dirts and eggs and to vacuum the surrounding area. Their food bowls should be washed daily. If dogs eat rotten food they can easily succumb to gastritis, and if the food has been around for a few days your animal may become infected with intestinal parasites. Your dog, especially if it is long-haired, will need help with its grooming. Brushing daily will remove excess knots and excess hair. A flea comb is most important to catch the flea population and in the height of summer you may need a flea collar or a spray.

HYPERTENSION

This may be due to colourants and additives in the food you are feeding so read the small print and buy the more expensive brands that do not contain them. Avoid raw or red meat and instead opt for cooked fish, vegetarian, vegan or macrobiotic diets. The dog may be lacking in potassium and calcium so bananas, broccoli, celery, cottage cheese, tomatoes and goat's milk should be given if it doesn't have a lactose intolerance. Chlorella is a good supplement and Bach's Rescue Remedy is good for immediate relief.

I is For:

IMMUNE SYSTEM

When the immune system is under par dogs, like humans, become prone to ailments and diseases. Balanced nutrition is the key to a healthy canine immune system. If you are feeding very pure organic foods either raw or lightly cooked there should be little need for supplements but if you are feeding cheap commercial foods your dog will probably need supplements. Over-vaccination may also harm the immune system. Some vets are now saying that vaccinating at three-yearly intervals is sufficient as antibodies from the previous vaccination can still be giving protection over that time span. Homoeopathic nosodes from a holistic vet can also be a healthy alternative to vaccination. However, in case of serious illness when conventional veterinary medicine has not made any headway, I have had enormous success with alternative medicines. Vitamin C (500–1000 mg daily depending on the size of the dog), stomach enzymes, organic garlic, canine antioxidants, essential oils, vitamins and minerals (either in powder or liquid form depending on the fragility of the digestive system) and echinacea are a daily requirement for any dog of mine with a health problem. However, I am pleased to say that as they are given supplements very regularly my vet's bills tend to be very small and infrequent.

INSECT BITES

If your dog is severely stung by bees or wasps as Sophie was when she disturbed a wasps' nest, you should take it to your vet as there may be an allergic reaction. Internally, *ledum palustre* may be appropriate. Externally, you can try to remove the sting with tweezers and then rub the area with *urtica urens* in liquid form. If the sting should become septic *chininum sulphuricum* and the herb echinacea may be helpful. A raw onion or garlic can take the smarting out of an insect bite if it is rubbed gently on the spot.

J is For:

JEALOUSY

Jealousy can be a major problem in dogs and it can be very stressful to everyone concerned. The jealousy is not necessarily another dog as often the dog is treated like the baby of the family until a real baby comes along. If it is then excluded it will naturally become upset and stressed, and can in certain instances become a dangerous animal.

The feelings of jealousy occur even more at the introduction of a new canine, particularly if it is an adult dog. If you are getting two dogs it may help to introduce them both to your home on the same day. That way there might be less territorial disputes as neither can claim prior ownership.

If you have two dogs and one dies do not presume that your old dog will like a newcomer. It will have had a particular relationship with your old dog which is not necessarily replaceable.

If you are replacing a dog and still have another, it is normally best to get a puppy, but they must not be left alone together until you are certain that the youngster has been accepted. There have been incidences of dogs killing new puppies when left unsupervised and there are occasions when the old dog will not accept the new puppy or dog at any level. In that case you will have to give up and find a new home for the newcomer. However, before you do that there are some homoeopathic and herbal remedies which can be tried.

Homoeopathically: *Staphisagria* can be used for jealousy. *Lachesis* is appropriate when there is a jealous nature and *arsenicum album* can be used when the dog is particularly possessive.

Herbally: Holly may help with dogs that are possessive, hate and are jealous. Beech is good for dogs who respond badly to change, in particular the introduction of a new dog or baby to the household and chicory can be given for egotistic, possessive, selfish canines who find it hard to share their owners.

The aromatherapy oils jasmine, ylang ylang and grapefruit may have a role to play with different kinds of jealousy.

K is For:

KENNEL COUGH

As the name implies this is a condition sometimes caught in kennels or from close proximity to other dogs, such as at shows or obedience classes. However, registered kennels demand the correct vaccination for infectious diseases and you can also get kennel cough nosodes from a holistic vet which can work very well. There is also an intranasal spray which takes five days to become effective, although the injectable vaccine is thought to provide immunity for a longer period. A veterinary cough supplement can be given for the harsh cough and antibiotics may be needed for chronic infections.

Nutritionally: Vitamin C, cod-liver oil and zinc supplements can help.

Herbally: Echinacea may help to boost the immune system and is best given in fortnightly doses, long term use is said not to be as effective.

KIDNEYS

There are good homoeopathic remedies available for kidney

infections such as *cantharis* which cured Daisy, my Dobermann who was thirteen at the time; *urtica urens* or *mer cor* can also help. However, in serious cases antibiotics may be necessary and your vet should be consulted. For an on-going problem a low protein diet is best with fish, poultry or rabbit, and carrots and broccoli as the main vegetables. Fluid levels need to be kept up to flush out the kidneys and pure water, barley water, diluted cranberry juice (two thirds water to one third juice) or concentrated cranberry tincture added to the dog's drinking water can be given. Yeast should be avoided but vitamins C, Bs, cod-liver oil and greenleaf tablets can help.

L is For:

LIVER

The liver is one of the most important organs in the body and a healthy liver is crucial to the well-being of a dog. You can help by feeding a high fibre/low fat diet with plenty of fish, wholemeal bread and brown rice and by avoiding milk, eggs and red meat. Sesame seeds are a particularly good source of lecithin which is vital for the liver, so you can sprinkle some seeds or add tahini to flavour dishes. Extra bulk and fibre can be made up with oatbran or rice bran and wheatgerm. A little beetroot, parsley, garlic, dandelion or milk thistle may also be helpful. Fasting once a week can be beneficial and the only drinks should be bottled water or barley water and honey. Sunshine may also be helpful to a dog with impaired liver function. Signs of liver problems are usually pale stools, sickness, diarrhoea and a refusal of food. If the whites of the eyes or gums are yellow the dog probably has jaundice. Severe liver disease may mean dark stools accompanied by blood.
Nutritionally: Vitamin C (500–1000 mg depending upon the size of the dog), coenzyme Q10 10 mg, cod-liver oil (quarter of a teaspoon), digestive enzymes and aloe vera could be beneficial.
Homoeopathically: George MacLeod recommends *phosphorus* if the stools are clay-coloured and *chelidonium* if the faeces are golden yellow. He suggests *lycopodium* for more chronic cases, *berberis* if there is loin weakness with pungent urine and *chionanthus* for jaundice with putty-like stools. For cirrhosis when there is consti-

pation, sickness and fluid in the stomach he recommends (apart from *phosphorus*, *lycopodium* and *berberis*) *carduus mar* which is known to be good for this condition, and *ptelea* which may act like a drainage remedy.
Herbally: Give echinacea or camomile and mix diced dandelion leaves in with the food. Alternatively, silmarin (Milk Thistle) is a good tonic.

M is For:

MINERALS

People often talk about vitamins but not everybody realises that minerals have just as important a role to play in maintaining a healthy immune system. Many years ago there were lots of trace minerals (over seventy) in our soil which were absorbed by the plants which then went into the food chain. However, since the use of chemicals, including organo-phosphates, on the land, with overworking of the soil over a long period of time, all the minerals essential to our health are now virtually non-existent. Our food supply is seriously deficient in minerals. Every aspect of the body requires minerals and without them not only us but our animals, too, will have serious health problems. It was because I couldn't find a multi-mineral product for dogs that my vet formulated the Canine Care mineral supplement. At least now my own dogs are no longer minerally deficient.

MOPING

Dogs can very definitely mope. They can mope at a change of abode, a change of owner, the introduction of a new person or animal into the household and the loss of either a person or an animal from their immediate family.
Homoeopathically: Tim Couzens recommends *arsenicum album* for despair.
Bach Flower Remedies: Tim Couzens recommends gorse (*ulex europaeus*) for animals that seem to have given up the will to live often with severe health problems.
Aromatherapy: Nelly Grosjean, a doctor of aromatherapy and essential oils, suggests basil and sweet marjoram for depression.

Aromatherapy oils should *never* be put on a dog's skin or fur, but should be inhaled at a distance of at least one foot.

N is For:

NERVES

Dogs love regularity and consistency. You can get a young dog used to moving around between different places, but if an older one is moved after a long time in one place it will undergo stress. Puppies and dogs from rescue centres have invariably had a stressful time and should be treated with TLC (tender loving care).

Dogs can be ultra-sensitive and can be subject to depression as a result of some tragedy in their lives, and unless something is done to snap them out of it they can give up and die. They tend to be very loyal to their owners and can pine without them or mope if a companion dog dies.

Nutritionally: Foods that are calming are oats, barley and turkey with sufficient bonemeal (calcium), along with canine minerals and vitamins A, D, E, C 500–1000 mg, and the mineral zinc 15 mg. B complex vitamins are said to be good for depression.

Homoeopathically: St John's Wort (*hypericum*) helps depression and Francis Hunter recommends *scuttelaria* (skullcap) twice a day for a week for depressed animals. Dr Richard Pitcairn recommends *kali phos* for nervous animals. *Ignatia* is excellent for grieving animals and *arsenicum album* can help animals who are panicking.

Herbally: Vervain may aid depression, and camomile, hops and valerian are calming.

NEUTERING

Roaming dogs can be the scourge of any neighbourhood, so if you want to be popular with your neighbours I recommend that you have your male puppy neutered. Also un-neutered dogs tend to be more aggressive and may be more likely to fight.

The neutering operation is very simple but for any surgery I always ask for the best anaesthetic in case of an allergic reaction. To boost the immune system you can administer A, E, C and B complex vitamins and zinc before and after surgery. Vitamin E can be beneficial if scar tissue is itching.

Homoeopathically: After any operation you can give *arnica, hypericum, phosphorus* or Bach's Rescue Remedy. On any post-operation tissue you can use *calendula.*
Herbally: Echinacea liquid can be used.

NUTRITION

The basic dietary requirements are what foods to give, how much and how often. The best food to give is raw food (but it *must* be from a reliable, unconditional source) or home-cooked food. However, cooking depletes vitamins and minerals so canine supplements along with bonemeal may be added when the food has cooled down. Ideal proteins for dogs can be found in chicken, turkey, guinea fowl, pheasant, rabbit, liver (in small amounts not more than twice a week), lamb, beef, cod, halibut, skate, haddock, coley, plaice, bream, mackerel, pilchards, salmon and herring. Protein for vegetarian dogs is abundant in pulses, seeds and nuts (not peanuts), free-range eggs, goats' milk and goats' yoghurt. However, dogs can have allergies to dairy products so a calcium supplement can be beneficial. Good vegetables to give are broccoli, Brussels sprouts, cabbage, peas, beans, pumpkin and beetroot. A pinch of thyme, sage, rosemary or garlic can be a healthy flavour-some addition. For carbohydrates one can add millet, oats, rice, spelt and polenta (corn meal). Organic or free-range products are preferable, particularly for dogs with serious health problems. If you are feeding commercial foods you may find it a false economy to buy cheap cans with a lot of moisture. The ones like Hills, Butcher's, Eukanuba, Techni-Cal, Naturediet, Menu and the original Denes are more expensive but I find my dogs eat less because they are packed full of goodness. The small print on some cans itemises additives, colourants, preservatives and sugars (caramels) so make a point of steering clear of those. The same criteria applies to dried foods as the ones without colourants, sugars, additives or preservatives are more nutritious such as James Wellbeloved, John Burns, Nutro, Techni-Cal and Hills. Through your vet you can also obtain tins for specific diseases.

Always make sure there is plenty of freshly boiled, uncontaminated or bottled water near at hand to prevent dehydration.

How much and how often should I feed my dog? It is not a question that is easily answered, as it changes with differing circumstances. I remember my effete Yorkshire Terriers would only eat diced chicken in London, but the moment we took them on a walking holiday in the Lake District they reverted to their true terrier selves. They were so ravenous they even begged for crusts from our sandwiches. Back in my London flat with their daily walks in Hyde Park they returned to their usual pernickety selves. The experts' views on how much protein a dog should have in its daily ration vary considerably – from 18 per cent to 40 per cent. Mark Elliott advocates 40 per cent as a general rule. However, we believe that if a dog has too much protein without enough channelled physical activity, it can lead to destructive, hyperactive and, in some breeds, even vicious behaviour. Protein should not exceed 60 per cent of a dog's diet at any one time and fats no more than 5 per cent. A proper diet should include the essential elements – protein, carbohydrates, fats, vitamins and minerals – in the correct proportion. It is also important to strike the right balance between liquids and solids.

The amount of food needed to feed a dog varies according to its breed, age, lifestyle (active or sedentary, indoor or outdoor), state of health, and whether it is pregnant or not. Climate too is a factor as dogs need more food in cold weather. Metabolisms differ even between dogs of the same size, so it would be impossible to calculate precisely how much food to give your dog. A rough guideline would be to say one ounce (30g) of food per day for every pound of a dog's weight – e.g. a dog weighing 20lbs (9kg), would need approx 1lb 4 oz (570g) of food per day.

A 20lb adult dog would need approximately 680 calories daily. So adjust recipes accordingly when cooking for your dog. As a dog's digestive system works on the basis of 6 plus hours, whereas a human's works on 20 plus hours, a dog doesn't need as many meals as we do. An average-sized dog should be served one meal a day, preferably in the morning, or 75 per cent of its meal in the morning and 25 per cent in the afternoon. Smaller breeds seem to prefer two meals a day. Most of us are brought up to feed our dogs their main meal in the late afternoon/early evening, which means they need to relieve themselves about midnight. This is rarely feasible because most people don't walk their dogs at that hour, and since they have been trained not to relieve themselves in the house a large number of pets end up at the vet's with anal problems. Avoid feeding a meal directly before or after exercise – a dog can't digest its food properly when it is tired and overheated. Never feed your dog hot food and never straight from the refrigerator; room temperature is best. If you are cooking for your dog it is advisable to store the food in the fridge because the food will not contain preservatives. Buying and cooking in bulk and freezing the food can prove economical both in terms of time and money. However, on no account should you freeze any cooked fish and never refreeze any food. In case your dog is sensitive to aluminium, use cast-iron, stainless steel or ceramic pots and pans. For optimum nutrition, with home-cooking I always add calcium (this can be bonemeal or crushed egg shell), rotating the vitamins, minerals, essential oils and antioxidants and varying the menus. That way I can be sure my dogs are getting everything they need to be healthy canines.

O is For:

OBESITY

An obese dog is a potentially unhealthy dog so if your dog is fat you would be well advised to put it on a diet. The first thing to do is to see whether the commercial food you may be feeding contains either 'sugars' or 'caramels' in the small print. If it does switch to one that doesn't have these additives, like Denes or Naturediet. The second thing is not to overfeed; in the wild it is unlikely that dogs would have been sitting down to a huge meal twice a day. You can add bulk to the food with oatbran and wheatgerm.

ORPHANS

It is very hard to perform all the functions that a bitch does for her puppy. She keeps them warm with her body, she cleans and stimulates them with her tongue and she feeds them with her milk, which if she has been vaccinated will give the puppies antibodies against diseases until they are fit enough to have vaccinations themselves.

For warmth you can give a hot-water bottle (reheated regularly), a microwave heat pad, or an electric pad (with a circuit breaker for safety) or a plastic bed with a heater inside it on which you can put a towel or vet bed. Young puppies lose body heat very easily so they must be kept warm.

I would not want to bathe a puppy in case it got chilled, however if the puppy fell into a toxic substance like oil one would of course wash it and dry it thoroughly afterwards. It is difficult feeding orphaned puppies as nothing is as good as mother's milk but when they are very tiny you can use small droppers or syringes to feed them. I advocate goats' milk as the most acceptable food for the very young. When they are first born they require feeding approximately every two hours, day and night, so it is very tiring work indeed.

P is For:

PARASITES

There are over eighty kinds of parasites that can affect dogs. Fortunately most of them are uncommon and often only found in foreign countries. However, the following can be quite common:

> *Anclystoma caninum* – the canine hookworm, generally symptomless in adults, but the following symptoms found in puppies may be present: anaemia (look for pale gums), diarrhoea with weakness and poor growth. A vet should be called as the animal could die if left untreated.
>
> *Dipylidium caninum* – common tapeworm of dogs, the flea is the intermediate host which the dog accidentally ingests whilst grooming. Tapeworm tablets can be obtained from vets or pet stores.
>
> *Giardia duodenalis* – giardiasis affects many mammals including humans. It is difficult to diagnose and usually causes self-limiting diarrhoea. However, it can be dangerous in young puppies. Signs are soft stools which may have mucus, or chronic diarrhoea. The animal should be seen by a vet who may advice fasting and/or drugs.
>
> *Isospora canis* – and *isospora ohionensis* cause the disease known as coccidiosis. A vet should be consulted speedily as it can prove fatal in young animals.

Taenia pisiformis – the common tapeworm of dogs. Rabbits and rodents are the intermediate host and when the dog eats the infected animal it in turn becomes infected. A tapeworm tablet should get rid of the problem until the next time.

Toxascaris leonina – is the less prominent roundworm in dogs and can also be found in cats. A roundworm tablet should expel the worms.

Toxacara canis – is the most prominent roundworm in dogs and it is also found in foxes. If one lives in a house with dogs it may be advisable, especially if you have children, to de-worm the family with an over-the-counter wormer from time to time such as Ovex or Pripsen. I find sulphur and garlic most effective worm deterrents. I also de-worm all my animals with a veterinary roundwormer at least every six months and if they are scavengers every 12 weeks.

Trichuris vulpis – the whipworm. Light infections will not produce any signs of illness but heavy infestations can produce smelly diarrhoea, sometimes with blood and mucus. A vet should be consulted.

PERITONITIS

This can be a fatal condition and you should demand instant veterinary attention, as well as blood tests and X-rays. When Kipling, my young Dobermann, was ill the hair stood up on his back, he had an uncomfortable hunched walk, he stopped eating and, finally, I saw blood in his motions. His condition was mis-diagnosed for seven days. 'It's gastro-enteritis,' was the vet's verdict one day, then: 'It's an enlarged prostate.' When he died on the operating table a week later the vet said, 'If we'd got the diagnosis right on the first day, he'd still be here.' That was little comfort, so act quickly.
Homoeopathically: *Cantharis, carduus mar* and *tub bov* could be beneficial. *Arsenicum album* 6c would be appropriate if the dog was restless, cold and drinking a lot. *Mercurius sulphuricus* could help if there was trouble with breathing.
Herbally: Give echinacea to boost the immune system.

Diane Stein suggests that as much as 100 mg of vitamin C can be given per hour for puppies and 250 mg per hour for adult dogs. I would also supplement with half a teaspoon of cod-liver oil combined with vitamin E 100 iu, a vitamin B complex and zinc 15 mg.
Nutritionally: Home-cooked food consisting predominantly of chicken, turkey, or rabbit with a little rice, broccoli, cabbage and beetroot with chicken liver twice a week.

POISONING

Potential dangers are everywhere but the most common cause seems to be weed-killer for lawns. Try not to use toxic weed-killers yourself and ask your neighbours to let you know when they are spraying so you can keep your pet in.

Other harmful poisons are some disinfectants and some plants, also woodworm and dry rot treatments. Some decorative plants are a problem, other hazards are insecticides and antifreeze (which is sweet to drink); bits of string and electric cables are other hazards.

If you need to induce vomiting you can place salt on the back of the tongue.

Anti-pollution vitamins and minerals are: A, C, calcium, selenium, zinc and kelp.
Homoeopathically: Give *nux vom*, or, for particularly toxic substances, *arsenicum album.*
Herbally: Slippery elm and aloe vera may be helpful.

R is For:

RENAL FAILURE

One always tends to blame oneself if a dog dies. Had I known the signs and had I known then what I know now there are certainly things that I could have done for Blue, my first Dobermann, which might well have prolonged his life. I did not know for instance about the colourants, additives, sugars and preservatives in some commercial foods as I never bothered to read the small print. I also did not know that some dried foods may cause dehydration and kidney problems in older dogs that drink too little, particularly if the water source is not pure. What I should have done is cooked a little protein such as chicken or turkey with some white rice and broccoli, given a vitamin B complex (10 mg), vitamin C (500–1000 mg depending on the size of the dog), vitamin A (1000 iu daily) and calcium (250 mg daily) possibly in crushed egg shell form. A little barley water or cranberry juice, one part to three parts water could also have been given or a few drops of concentrated cranberry tincture added to the dog's drinking water.

Homoeopathically: *Nux vomica* helps with toxicity and sickness and *nat mur* may be appropriate if the dog is showing signs of thirst.

Herbally: Alfalfa or greenleaf tablets can be given with food.

If you do not have time to cook you may find there is a specially prepared food for kidney problems available from your vet.

RINGWORM

Ringworm is an uncommon problem but does occur sometimes and should be dealt with quickly as it can spread to other animals and people. It is in fact a fungus not a worm and grows in the shape of a circle infecting the hair and skin in that area.

Homoeopathically: *Sulphur* should be given.

Herbally: Richard Pitcairn recommends a brew of plantago major or an infusion of hydrastis canadiensis which can be rubbed in twice a day.

If there is still a problem consult a veterinarian.

S is For:

SPAYING

Do please take this issue seriously as there are so many unwanted dogs around that the rescue centres cannot cope with the volume. A female should be spayed at the age of six months and even then you should be alert for signs of an early heat. There are several other good reasons for spaying:

1) You will not attract dogs to your area.
2) A bitch that is bred too often will get debilitated.
3) The bitch will no longer have the possibility of pyometria and the chances of getting breast cancer may be reduced.

With the over-population of canines and the euthanasia of so many unwanted pets do you want your dog's offspring to contribute to those numbers? Your dog would be responsible for thousands of unwanted canines in just a few years. It is also cheaper to spay your bitch than to pay for the cost of building up the mother dog and feeding her puppies over eight weeks, not to mention the cost of worming and possibly veterinary bills. Spaying is by far the cheapest – and kindest – option.

SURGERY

Before an operation give *arnica* and C, E and B vitamins, and minerals to boost the immune system. A dog should be starved for at least twelve hours before an operation.

After surgery continue to give C, E and B vitamins and minerals along with pure foods to quicken the recovery and to speed up healing. Rub either *arnica* or *calendula* creams on the scar. If the dog scratches at the wound it may be necessary to get a collar (the shape of a lampshade) from the vet to prevent it reaching the affected area.

T is For:

TATT (TIRED ALL THE TIME)

'You are what you eat.' If your dog is showing signs of lethargy make sure you are feeding good quality, nutritious food. If you are feeding it commercial canned food, check the small print and change to an additive-free, vitamin-rich brand. It could be suffering from a lack of folic acid, in which case add green vegetables, lentils, oats and wheatgerm to its diet or a folic acid pill. You can increase the dogs intake of iron by giving liver, kidneys, sunflower and sesame seeds, and various pulses. Extra supplements that are helpful are a vitamin B complex, vitamin C, chlorella, kelp, betacarotene, the herb gentian and *arnica*. Daisy, my Dobermann, slept a lot more in her old age and I used to give her extra vitamin C (500 twice a day), Canine Care antioxidants, a vitamin and mineral supplement and essential oils.

TEETH

If you want your dog to have good teeth the first thing is to avoid some of the sugary commercial foods. Nutritionally, calcium and phosphorus in food is important for tooth development and vitamins and minerals help maintain healthy gums. Raw bones (from a non-salmonella source) or some dry biscuit can aid in cleaning teeth, as indeed can a toothbrush.

Homoeopathically: *Calc fluor* is the appropriate remedy.

Herbally: Myrrh and echinacea in liquid form make a good mouthwash.

U is For:

URINARY INFECTIONS

Urinary infections usually become obvious when the dog has trouble urinating, or passes blood, or it may also start to pee in unfamiliar places. Some vets suspect that urinary tract disease may be due to feeding dry commercial foods over a long period of time. It is advisable to stop immediately and the dog should be given chicken, turkey or rabbit with green vegetables or if necessary a very pure brand free from additives, preservatives, colourants and sugars.

Vitamins C (500–1000 mg), E (50 iu), a B complex (20 mg) without yeast and a quarter of a teaspoon of cod-liver oil should be given daily. When the condition subsides a daily intake of a canine multi-vitamin-mineral powder and antioxidant should be maintained along with vitamin C (100 mg) and a quarter of a teaspoon of cod-liver oil twice a week.

When Roscoe repeatedly had cystitis and I wormed him the problem stopped, so check that a worm infestation isn't the cause.

Homoeopathically: *Cantharis, sasparilla, urtica urens, merc cor, pulsatilla* or *nux vomica* alleviate the symptoms. *Sepia, apis mel, berberis* and *equisetum* can also be beneficial.

Herbally: Cranberry juice diluted one part to three parts water or barley water can help. Parsley is also a good diuretic.

However, if your dog is in obvious distress and its condition has become acute you should see a vet as quickly as possible. If it is urinating frequently and drinking a great deal you should also have the animal checked for diabetes.

V is For:

VACCINATIONS

The most recent veterinary thinking, from the American Small Animal Veterinary Association, is that antibodies from vaccinations stay in the system for up to three years so annual vaccinations may be unnecessary. The main trouble is that boarding kennels demand a recent vaccination, but that edict really should be changed. If you have any doubts go to a homoeopathic vet and ask for the homoeopathic alternative. According to Richard Allport, the homoeopathic vet at the Natural Medicine Veterinary Centre 'Most veterinary surgeons in conventional practice feel that the normal vaccinations are, on the whole, safe and effective; but the majority of homoeopathic vets have serious worries about the effect of conventional vaccines on the immune system'. He adds, 'There seems a strong possibility that conventional vaccines may be a factor in the development of chronic diseases such as eczema, colitis and auto-immune conditions'.

A puppy's immune system can still be very delicate and if the mother has been vaccinated recently it will have antibodies from that vaccination in its blood for a time anyway. All animals should be in optimum condition before vaccinating.

Ever since my young Dobermann became very ill with a runny nose and cough after a vaccination I have been very wary of having my dogs vaccinated. It was therefore with great interest that I read Catherine O'Driscoll's book on vaccination, *Who Killed the Darling Buds of May?* According to one vaccine manufacturer only fifteen dogs in three million had adverse reactions from doses. Catherine found out that all her six dogs had developed diseases – thyroid, arthritis, leukaemia, paralysis and death, cancer and allergies – all of which were associated by scientific heavyweights with vaccine damage. Six out of six was certainly not the odds the vaccine manufacturers claimed.

However, the vaccine manufacturers advise vets that adverse reactions might occur if:

- the dog is genetically defective
- there is something wrong with the dog's diet
- the dog was unhealthy when vaccinated

- the dog was stressed at the time of the injection
- the dog's immune system is incompetent
- the dog is exposed to the virus within a given time-frame after vaccination
- the dog is taking immune-suppressive drugs
- the vet stores and handles the vaccine inappropriately
- a puppy still has the maternal anti-body in its system, which could interfere with the effectiveness of the vaccine.

According to Catherine's experience the adverse reaction may not manifest itself immediately but can appear a few months later. So beware and think carefully before you vaccinate your dog, particularly on a regular, annual basis.

VITAMINS

All too often there are inadequacies in a dog's diet. A canine multivitamin with minerals is designed to fill the nutritional gap between modern diets and a dog's daily needs, promoting optimum health and longevity. A balanced formulation like the Canine Care vitamin and mineral supplement contains kelp and green barley to fulfil a dog's need for chlorophyll and iodine. It also contains digestive enzymes for optimum digestion. A good canine vitamin-mineral supplement is insurance that your dog is getting its necessary daily quota of healthy vitamins, especially if you are feeding it the cheaper commercial brands.

W is For:

WORMING

If you see what looks like long (usually up to half an inch) pieces of rice stuck to your dog's rear end or in its faeces they may well prove to be segments of tapeworm that have broken away. The wormers that I prefer are Endorid for roundworms (which can be given in two doses over two weeks), Drontal for roundworm and tapeworm and Panacur granules which cover roundworm and tapeworm in dogs and also treats giardia in weaned puppies. It is important to keep on top of the flea problem as worms are passed on to the dog via the flea, if your dog accidentally swallows a flea whilst grooming itself this may start up worms again. In an old dog it may be advisable to give a digestive enzyme with food after worming.

Homoeopathically: For tapeworms you can give *felix mas* or *merc cor* (when the dog is passing blood in its faeces). For roundworms give *cina* or *chenopodium.*

Herbally: Hawthorn may be helpful. Oatbran and garlic are not liked by worms and should be mixed in with a pure diet of optimum nutrition.

A little rock sulphur in your dog's drinking water may also deter ticks and fleas, particularly in summer.

In her book *The Complete Herbal Handbook for the Dog and Cat* the herbalist Juliette de Bairacli Levy is adamant that chemical wormer drugs should not be used on puppies or adults. For tapeworms she recommends a day and night of fasting followed by small round cakes containing fresh rue, wormwood and cayenne pepper (of the hottest variety). One part of the first two ingredients to two parts pepper, bound together with thick honey and flour made into a tablespoon of the mixture. This can then be pressed into small cakes and pushed down the throat. After half an hour she recommends a strong dose of castor oil or Epsom salts. She says Tabasco sauce is a safe concentration of cayenne and can be used with fifteen to twenty drops mixed into the flour and honey for an average-sized dog.

For roundworms she advocates a fast of one day for a young puppy while giving water with a little honey (one teaspoon per bowl for an average puppy) and two days for a six-month-old or adult puppy. On the night of the fast they should be given a strong dose of castor oil (one dessertspoon for an average-sized puppy under six months, less for a puppy under three months) and one and a half tablespoons for an adult Cocker-sized dog, and two tablespoons for an adult Greyhound-type dog.

The following day, six to eight three-grain tablets with garlic, rue or eucalyptus or other herbal worming tablets should be given. Thirty minutes later another laxative dose of castor oil should be given and thirty minutes later a laxative feed in a semi-liquid mixture of milk thickened with tree-bark's flour, honey and flaked oats.

In a dog's daily diet she suggests one or two of the following worm-removing aids at a time: grated raw coconut, grated raw carrot, ground pumpkin seeds (raw), cut seeds (raw) of nasturtium and papaya, whole grapeseeds, whole melon pips or finely chopped garlic. One teaspoon of the above for an average-sized puppy and one dessertspoon for a Cocker-sized adult, given twice daily.

Francis Hunter homoeopathic veterinary surgeon and acupuncturist writes:

> I have to disagree with what Juliette de Bairacli Levy writes on the subject of worming in the extract above taken from *The Complete Herbal Handbook for the Dog and Cat.*
>
> i. Roundworms: Over a period of more than 40 years in general veterinary practice I can say that worming products have improved enormously during the last 10–15 years in both efficiency and the possible adverse reaction that they might have on the animals being dosed with them. Roundworm treatments on the whole are now quite gentle in their action and are extremely effective. Worming does not have to be carried out so frequently that long-standing side-effects (such as with prolonged use of antibiotics or steroids) are likely.
>
> I feel that it is quite wrong and potentially more harmful to starve a young puppy for one or two days. I cannot agree that it is right to withhold meals from animals of any age or species. Animals live by routine and cannot understand why they are not receiving regular feeding. Moreover the thought of giving any animals castor oil appals me.
>
> ii. Tapeworms: Tapeworms are more difficult to remove because the head has to be dislodged from the intestinal lining of the host, which calls for harsher remedies. Here again modern treatments are very effective and adverse reactions few.
>
> Worming is very important and it is my opinion that it is preferable to consult your veterinary surgeon and obtain modern treatments, rather than purchasing patent medicines over the counter.

It is interesting to note that Juliette de Bairacli Levy's book was written over 15 years ago, while Francis Hunter's comments are obviously much more recent.

(Please note that if your dog shows any signs of illness, you must first consult your vet. The above suggestions are merely 'healthy hints', to be used only in conjunction with your vet's advice after consultation.)

X is For:

XENOPHOBIA (FEAR OF FOREIGNERS)

Nutritionally turkey is the most calming of meats along with vegetarian meals.
Homoeopathically: *Hyoscyamus* is used a lot on dogs who are suspicious of people. *Lycopodium* is the appropriate remedy for domestic dogs who hate most strangers.
Herbally: Bach's Rescue Remedy may calm a dog down that is stressed by someone new and impatiens can be very calming.

X-RAY

X-rays are a very valuable diagnostic aid particularly with bone problems or digestive disorders caused by an obstruction. If you are worried that your dog has been exposed to too much radiation give vitamin C (up to 1000 mg a day depending on the size of dog), kelp, bioflavanoids and vitamin Bs.

Y is For:

YEAST

Some animals have a yeast allergy, in which case foods such as bread and mushrooms should be avoided, although you can buy soda bread which is not made with yeast. Also some people and some animals have an allergy to the new DNA altered wheat and may fare better with old-fashioned organic wheat. However, if your dog does not have a yeast allergy a small amount of brewer's yeast, which canines often find very tasty, is a useful source of the B vitamins which are particularly good for the nervous system.

Z is For:

ZINC

Zinc is one of the most valuable minerals in boosting the immune system. It used to be found in the soil and passed on to the food chain but it is now sadly lacking as most of our fields are overworked and are regularly sprayed with pesticides and chemicals. An animal with skin or coat problems may well be deficient in zinc and should be given a zinc tablet internally while a zinc ointment can be used externally. Zinc is a bactericide and can be used after surgery or on burns. Zinc also helps to repair tissue and to make the immune system function properly. It should be given as a supplement in all the major canine illnesses including cancer. It is a mineral which should be taken separately from the others and does not need to be taken with food.

COMMERCIAL DOG FOOD

'Roy wanted to tell his father the truth about the Space Dog, but he had to hold his tongue. He was the only one who knew that Space Dog never ate a bit of the dog food that the Barneses bought. He ate people food. Roy secretly threw the dog food away.'

from *Space Dog the Hero*
by Natalie Standiford

Most of us are guilty of leading an instant 'ready-made' life, and we have been persuaded by the pet food industry through its seductive advertising to include our dogs in that 'instant' formula. How much easier to open a tin or sack of dried food than actually to spend time toiling over the oven for our precious pooches.

Since researching the available pet foods for this book I have found it very hard to find products that I find acceptable for my dogs. Apart from 'with lamb' or 'with chicken' advertised in big letters on the front, have you ever looked at the small print on the back? We suggest, in fairness to your dog, that you start now – and warn you that you are in for a surprise! From October 1997 the pet food companies will be obliged to put the percentage of the meat advertised in the small print and this will have to be a minimum of four per cent. However, a tin contains 100 per cent, so on the whole 96 per cent you will read contains 'animal derivatives', 'animal by-products', sometimes 'vegetable derivatives', moisture and often caramel, colourants and additives.

Prior to the BSE scandal most people, like myself with poultry, were unaware of what they were feeding their animals – namely scrapie-infected dead sheep. We are appalled that the pet food industry, on the whole, will not let us know what we are feeding our dogs. Why not? Would we be so shocked that we would stop buying instant foods and start cooking real meat, vegetables and grains? Surely that can be the only reason.

In the *Earth Island Journal* (Fall 1990 and Summer 1996) which is published in the USA, they ran articles explaining how euthanased dogs and cats were sent to the pet food rendering plants. There, incredibly, they were boiled up with the other miscellanea from the meat industry and put into pet foods. I am not suggesting that this has happened in the UK, but I would still like to know precisely what 'animal derivatives' and 'by-products' actually are.

However, we were startled to read the following excerpt taken from a piece entitled 'Pet Food Theory Over Dog in BSE Alert' which appeared in the *Daily Mail* on Tuesday, 22 April 1997:

> Scientists are investigating what might be the first case of mad cow disease transferring to a pet dog. A post mortem examination on an 11-year-old golden retriever found changes in the brain which are similar to those seen in infected cows and

> humans. The dog was owned by a family in Norway, where scientists believe the BSE could have come from canned food imported from the UK. Norway imports most of its dog and cat food from England. Before 1994 there was no quality inspection. There are question marks over the theory, however. For while more than 70 per cent of cats are known to have developed the disease in Britain, no dog has been diagnosed.
>
> The pet food industry acted quickly to ensure infected material was not included in the mix after BSE was first recognised. Manufacturers stopped using offal which included potentially infectious BSE material in April 1989.

If you look carefully you will find that some instant pet foods are better than others and we would strongly advise you to search them out. Some, like Butcher's Tripe, contain 26 per cent tripe and no additives or colourants and others, like Hill's Science Diet, have far more vitamins and minerals. Semi-moist foods often contain a lot of sugar and textured soya and dried foods also vary enormously in quality.

Unfortunately you tend to get what you pay for. Puppies and pregnant bitches should be on a high-protein diet, so Techni-Cal, Hills, Eukanuba, Menu or Nutro would be good brands to use.

When you realise that you are paying for only 4 per cent of what is advertised on the front, suddenly cooking for your dog becomes a lot more economical. The very good news is that an organic, tinned dog food, one hundred per cent pure, has now arrived on the market, and is available from the better health stores, pet shops and Tesco.

CANINE CUISINE

MEATY MEALS

'He is my dog, Toto,' answered Dorothy.
'Is he made of tin, or stuffed?' asked the Lion.
'Neither. He's a-a-a meat dog,' said the girl.

from *The Wizard of Oz*
by L. Frank Baum

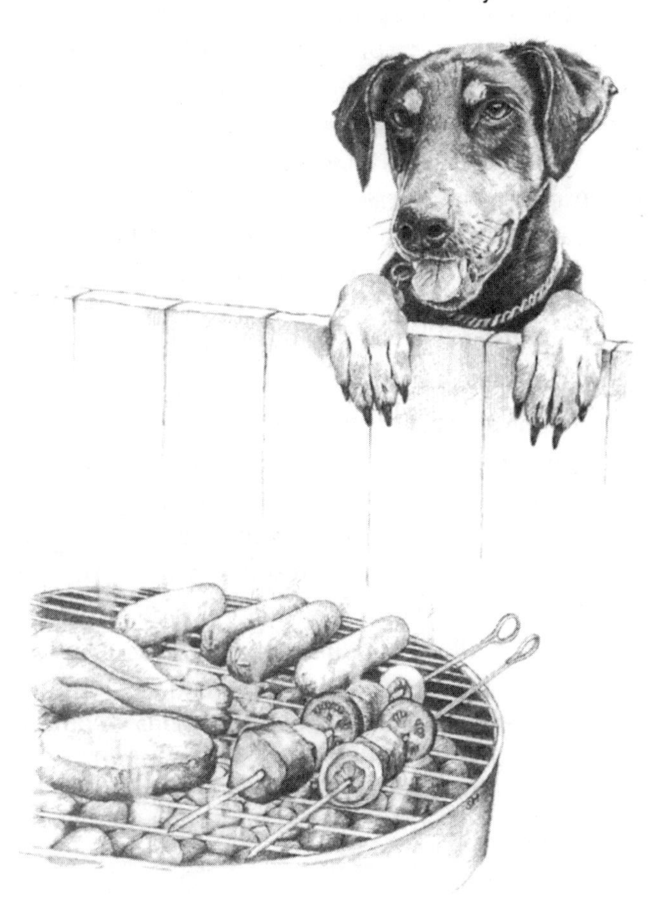

Dogs are predominantly carnivorous; however they can be vegetarian, vegan or macrobiotic if given a balanced diet. Equally they should never be fed an exclusively meat-only diet, as this would be nutritionally deficient. In the wild, dogs would have caught and devoured small animals, eating not just the meat but also the bones, fur, liver, heart, kidneys etc. and the grains digested by their prey. They would also have eaten available fruit and berries, grasses and trace minerals from other animals' dung.

In order for dogs to be healthy therefore, meat should not comprise more than 70 per cent of their diet. Given the worries about BSE in beef, and scrapie in sheep, not to mention the addition of antibiotics and growth hormones, we recommend kind food meat. At the back of the book we have included the address of the Soil Association from whom you can obtain the *Soil Association Directory of Organic Farm Shops and Box Schemes*.

Obesity can be a major problem for dogs as it can lead to heart, liver, kidney, thyroid, diabetic and intestinal problems so always pick lean meat and scale down the recipe according to the size of your dog. A little oatbran and wheatgerm (vitamin B) can help provide bulk and also aid digestion (one teaspoon for the average dog).

Occasionally raw meat is very worthwhile as it makes the intestines work properly, but it should not be given to a hyperactive or aggressive dog. Marrow bones provide calcium and phosphorus, and liver is occasionally beneficial as it contains folic acid.

In catering for canines one should try and imitate nature as much as possible and rotate the menus. That way dogs get a varied, vitamin and mineral-rich diet.

If you have a word with your local butcher and tell him that you are cooking for your dog, the chances are he will be happy to let you have various off-cuts and bones at a reduced price. He may also stock frozen pet mince as do various pet shops – ox cheeks, green tripe, tripe and chicken, tripe and beef, beef, chicken, lamb, turkey and rabbit.

Allen's, the butchers in Mayfair, was my Dobermann Blue's favourite shop and whenever we were in the vicinity he would drag me there on the end of his lead. He knew they were always keeping food for him and if he proffered his paw, they would give him the odd choice morsel.

MEATY BREW

'You can never scare a dog away from a greasy hide.'
'Canis a corio nunquam absterrebitur uncto.'

from *Satires* (II, v, 83)
by Quintus Hòratius Flaccus Horace

16 oz (455g) any combination of beef/lamb/chicken and rabbit (meat, bones, gristle, offal)
40 fl oz (2 pints UK/2½ pints USA) cold water
1 teaspoon Bovril (or Marmite Yeast Extract, Vegemite or Vitamite)
½ teaspoon wheatgerm oil
1 carrot, sliced
½ onion, sliced
1 turnip, sliced

Put the meat, bones, Bovril or Marmite and wheatgerm oil in a saucepan with cold water. Cover and bring to the boil. Simmer for one hour, or longer if you want to have more gelatine and calcium drawn out of the bones and meat. Add vegetables, bring to the boil and simmer for a further 30 minutes. Strain. If the meat was fatty, skim off the excess fat when it has cooled

MEAT & VEG PÂTÉ

'Waste not, want not.'
Proverb

Remove the meat from the bones (discard bones). Mix the vegetables and meat together and put in the blender. Work until you have a smooth consistency. Mix this with cooked brown rice or wholemeal bread and you'll have another couple of meals.

RISE 'N' SHINE

'A Dog starved at his Master's Gate
Predicts the ruin of the State.'

from *Auguries of Innocence*
by William Blake

3 oz (85g/1 cup) Scottish whole rolled porridge oats
10 fl oz (285ml/1¼ cups) boiling water
1 oz (30g) chicken livers
½ teaspoon extra virgin olive oil
1 teaspoon honey
1 oz (30g/⅓ cup) raisins (optional)
1 teaspoon brewer's yeast
half a kelp tablet, crushed

Pour the boiling water over the porridge oats and stir continuously for four minutes. Meanwhile, fry the chicken livers in the olive oil for three to four minutes. Add the honey, raisins, brewer's yeast, kelp tablet and cooked chicken livers to the porridge oats.

If you have an egg for breakfast, crush the shell into powder and sprinkle on top of Rise 'n' Shine for added calcium.

In cold weather as an extra treat you may like to sprinkle on a few sunflower seeds to give some added fat.

RUFUS' ROAST

Sir Winston Churchill had a Poodle called Rufus. Every evening when the family sat down to dinner, Rufus' personal cloth was put down and he was always served first.

4 oz (115g) stewing steak
2 slices (3 oz/85g) wholemeal bread
1 medium-sized carrot, sliced
1 oz (30g) onion, chopped (optional)
1 clove garlic, crushed (optional)
5 fl oz (140ml/¾ cup) Meaty Brew (page 73)

Chop up the steak, slice the bread and break into small chunks. Mix together the meat, bread, carrot, onion and garlic. Place in a greased casserole dish. Pour over Meaty Brew and bake at 350°F for 45 minutes.

Garlic improves a dog's appetite and the condition of its coat, as well as deterring worms and fleas.

DOGGIE BITES

'I loathe people who keep dogs. They are cowards who haven't got the guts to bite people themselves.'

from *A Madman's Discourse*
by August Strindberg

12 oz (340g/3 cups) organic stoneground wholemeal flour
4 oz (115g) minced lean meat (beef, chicken, turkey or lamb)
or 4 oz (115g) puréed cooked vegetables
or 4 oz (115g) Meat and Veg Pâté (page 73)
1 free-range egg, beaten
1 tablespoon unrefined safflower oil
5 fl oz (140ml/¾ cup) Meaty Brew (page 73)

Mix the minced meat *or* puréed vegetables *or* Meat & Veg Pâté with the flour until it looks like stiff breadcrumbs. Beat together the egg and safflower oil and add to flour mixture. Add Meaty Brew to create the consistency of dough which you can then roll out on a floured board to approximately ¼ inch thick. Cut with a small gingerbread man or cat-shaped cutter. Place Doggie Bites on a greased baking tray and bake at 300°F for 1 hour and 20 minutes. Allow them to cool on the tray.

Safflower oil has more linoleic acid than any other oil (up to 80 per cent) which may help to lower the cholesterol level in the blood.

LUIS' GUK

Jeannie says: 'If my father, Luis, was ever left with instructions by my mother to "feed the dogs", this is what they got whether they liked it or not (and so did we, I seem to remember!); but judging by how Shandy and Brandy, our yellow Labrador Retriever and English Springer Spaniel, always golloped up guk, it was a firm favourite.'

4 oz (115g) lean minced beef
1 teaspoon unrefined corn oil
a pinch of chilli powder or a drop of Tabasco pepper sauce (optional)
1 tin (198g) Heinz macaroni cheese
½ oz (15g) carrot, grated
a handful of Crunchy Crumbs (page 133)

Fry the beef in corn oil until brown. Add the chilli powder or Tabasco pepper sauce and macaroni cheese. Heat to room temperature. Mix grated carrot with a handful of Crunchy Crumbs and sprinkle on top.

Corn or maize oil is a popular cooking oil because it is light and easy to digest. Corn is a good source of phosphorus, vitamins A, D and E and the oil contains up to 53 per cent linoleic acid. The Peruvians started pressing corn for its valuable oil thousands of years ago and vets often recommend it to be taken internally and externally for skin problems.

BEETHOVEN'S SPAGHETTI PRELUDE

Beethoven, the St Bernard featured in a popular Hollywood film, wreaked havoc in the home of the family he adopted. Many comic situations resulted of which Charlie Chaplin would no doubt have approved – he always wanted 'a dog that would be hungry enough to be funny for his feed'.

Beethoven had a bottomless pit for a stomach; hence this dish would have merely been 'starters' for Beethoven.

1 teaspoon unrefined vegetable oil
1 oz (30g) onion, chopped
½ clove garlic, crushed
1 bay leaf
4 oz (115g) minced beef
½ oz (15g) carrot, grated
½ oz (15g) broccoli, diced
1 tomato, peeled & chopped (2–3 oz/55–85g)
½ teaspoon tomato purée
3½ fl oz (100ml/⅓ cup) Meaty Brew (page 73)
2 oz (55g) wholewheat spaghetti, cooked in boiling water for eight to ten minutes
½ teaspoon Parmesan cheese, grated (optional)

Fry the onion, garlic and bay leaf in vegetable oil for two to three minutes. Add the meat and fry for ten minutes on a low heat. Add carrot, broccoli, tomato, tomato purée and Meaty Brew. Let it boil for about five minutes while stirring constantly until the liquid has reduced – remove the bay leaf. Mix in the wholewheat spaghetti and sprinkle on Parmesan cheese.

Bay leaves are reputed to cure everything!

HOT FLUSH CHICKEN

Elizabeth Barrett Browning retrieved her beloved Spaniel called Flush from the hands of the dog-snatchers by paying an exorbitant ransom. Her maid recalls that:

'Flush was thereafter spoiled even more than usual for at least a week. If the mistress's dog wished to have finely chopped breast of chicken with just a touch of cayenne pepper on it then, why, she would chop it and pepper it and serve it to His Lordship.'

from *Lady's Maid*
by Margaret Forster

4 oz (115g) free-range chicken breast
½ teaspoon cornflour
a pinch of cayenne pepper
1½ fl oz (40ml) V8 juice
1 fl oz (30ml) pineapple juice
1 fl oz (30ml) Meaty Brew (page 73)
½ oz (15g) onion, chopped
2 oz (55g/⅓ cup) brown rice, cooked in boiling water for 30–35 minutes
or 5 oz (140g) mashed potato
1 oz (30g) Brussels sprouts, cooked and chopped

Cut the chicken into bite-sized pieces (use chicken bones to make Meaty Brew) and toss in the cornflour mixed with cayenne pepper. Place in a casserole dish. Heat up V8 juice, pineapple juice, Meaty Brew and onion in a saucepan. Bring to the boil and pour over the chicken. Cook covered in the oven at 300°F for 75 minutes. Mix with brown rice or mashed potato and Brussels sprouts.

MILD FLUSH CHICKEN

2 chicken drumsticks
2 pints water
1 teaspoon Marmite (or Vegemite, Vitamite or Yeast Extract)
3 oz (85g/½ cup) brown rice, uncooked
4 oz (115g) fresh corn or tinned sweetcorn (no sugar or salt added)
1 tablespoon cottage cheese

Put the chicken, water and Marmite in a saucepan. Bring to the boil. Simmer for 25 minutes. Add brown rice. Return to the boil. Simmer for a further 35 minutes. Drain (save liquid for making dog biscuits or flavouring a dry meal). Add the corn and cottage cheese. This recipe makes enough for two to three meals, depending on the size of your dog.

LANCASHIRE HEELER HOT-POT

The Lancashire Heeler is an ancient British breed, which is slowly disappearing, with fewer being registered annually at the Kennel Club. Instead foreign look-a-likes are being imported and there is great concern about saving our living heritage. But one bit of British heritage that will never die is Lancashire hot-pot!

2 oz (55g) lamb, chunks
2 oz (55g) kidneys, washed, white core removed, & chopped
6 oz (170g) potato, ½ sliced/½ cubed
1 oz onion, chopped
a pinch of rosemary, chopped
5 fl oz (140ml) Meaty Brew or liquid from Mild Flush Chicken (pages 73, 81)
1 oz (30g) Brussels sprouts, cooked

Put the sliced potato in the bottom of a greased casserole dish. Throw in the lamb and kidneys, followed by the onions and rosemary. Sprinkle the cubed potatoes on top. Pour over liquid. Cover and cook at 350°F for 1 hour 45 minutes. Add Brussels sprouts.

GIVE A DOG A BONE

'This old man, he played one,
He played nick nack on my drum;
Nick nack paddy wack give a dog a bone,
This old man came rolling home.'

from *This Old Man*
Traditional Nursery Rhyme

Dr Bruce Fogle, the London vet, recommends daily brushing of a dog's teeth with a toothbrush. However with the correct food (lacking in sugars and caramel) and an occasional bone, dogs' teeth should stay in reasonable condition all their lives.

A bone will provide the calcium, phosphorus and copper they need in their diet and the gnawing action of their teeth will remove any tartar that is building up. The Australian vet, Dr Ian

Billinghurst, recommends that you only feed your dog uncooked meaty bones, as that is what a dog would have eaten in the wild. However, we aren't sure about that. In nature dogs would have spent their day stalking and hunting their prey and fighting off other packs of dogs that strayed on to their territory. It would have been a very different existence from that of our domestic dogs today who, if they are lucky, are confined to a garden with one walk a day. Too much protein can make a dog hyperactive, which is not what is needed in a quiet domestic situation.

My dogs get a marrow bone or shank bone two or three times a week. These are the only bones that you can depend on not to splinter. Sophie, the Dobermann, once removed three pheasant carcasses from the saucepan on top of the cooker and survived to tell the tale. Other people's dogs have stolen poultry and ended up with splinters of bone in the intestines and expensive vets' bills for their owners.

If you have more than one dog you should remove the bones when they have lost interest, as they attract flies and can often provide an excuse for a squabble!

A shank bone can be given a new lease of life if you fill the hole with dog biscuits which they can spend several happy hours trying to get at.

Some vets recommend feeding your dog only water and a bone every ten days, as a fast which will cleanse the system. I've tried that with my dogs but it doesn't seem to work – they still seem to expect their main meal as well, although I can get away with down-sizing the portion!

> 'He tried to attract the attention of the dog by calling softly to it, and when the pomeranian came up to him he shook a finger at it. The pomeranian growled. Gurov again shook a finger at it.
>
> The woman looked up at him and immediately lowered her eyes.
>
> 'He doesn't bite,' she said and blushed.
>
> 'May I give him a bone?' he asked, and when she nodded, he said amiably: 'Have you been long in Yalta?'
>
> from *Lady With Lapdog*
> by Anton Chekhov

FISH FODDER

'As I was sayin', Henry, we've got six dogs. I took six fish out of the bag. I gave one fish to each dog, an', Henry, I was one fish short.'

'You counted wrong.'

from *White Fang*
by Jack London

Fish is not the natural food of dogs although Portuguese Water Spaniels, Newfoundlands, Huskies and Finnish Spitz would no doubt be given a fair amount of fish in their diets.

All fish are suitable for invalid diets, steamed or baked and served with rice, and are a good source of protein, magnesium, iodine and selenium. However, mackerel, herring, sardine and tuna are the best to serve as they have high levels of fatty acids which help to maintain a glossy coat. These fish preserve their goodness in tins with brine and can be given as an occasional (if expensive) treat. Coley is usually the cheapest fresh or frozen fish available. It is imperative to remove all the bones from fish. (Of course you could avoid bones by serving your dog squid, which in fact contains more protein than beef!) Another economical solution would be to buy minced cod, which can be found at some fish shops and is free from bone. Raw fish contains an enzyme called thiaminase, which destroys vitamin B1; however cooking fish kills off the thiaminase enzyme. Cooked fish should never be reheated, although it can be stored in a refrigerator for up to twenty-four hours.

FISH BREW

'Damned neuters in their middle way of steering,
are neither fish nor flesh nor good red-herring.'

Epilogue to *The Duke of Guise*
by John Dryden

16 oz (1 lb) (455g) fish (heads, tails, skin and bones)
1¼ litres cold water
1 carrot, chopped
1 onion, chopped
1 turnip, peeled and chopped
a stick of celery, sliced

Put the fish in a saucepan. Add the cold water. Bring to the boil and add the vegetables. Cover and simmer for 45 minutes – any longer and it will start to taste bitter. Strain the brew through a fine sieve.

SCIPIO PAELLA

'Scipio: It was just in the same way that I got into the house of the masters I served. It seems that we read men's thoughts.'

Miguel de Cervantes
from *Exemplary Novels*, 'Dialogue Between Two Dogs'
trans. Walter Kelly

½ oz (15g) bell pepper, chopped
½ oz (15g) onion, chopped
½ clove garlic, crushed
½ teaspoon unrefined sunflower oil
2 oz (55g/⅓ cup) brown rice, uncooked
1 oz (30g) peas, fresh or frozen
1 tomato, peeled and chopped
2 oz (55g) coley
2 oz (55g) whiting or cod
10 fl oz (285ml/1¼ cups) Fish Brew (page 88)

Fry the bell pepper, onion and garlic in sunflower oil for five minutes. Add the rice, peas, tomato, fish and Fish Brew. Bring to the boil. Cover and simmer for 30 minutes. Let the paella cool before extracting the fish – skin, flake and remove any bones. Return the fish to the mixture. (If you have any left-over cooked chicken, chop it up and add to the paella.)

If you take a taste of Scipio Paella, it's more than likely you will find yourself sharing this meal with your dog; in fact, it would be rude not to!

INDEPENDENCE DAY FISH

If your dog has been in kennels this makes a good easy-to-digest, welcome-home meal.

7 oz (200g) coley, whiting or cod, either separately or in a mixture
1½ oz (45g) fresh breadcrumbs using brown bread with malted grains
½ oz (15g) leek, finely sliced
1 oz (30g) broccoli, chopped
a pinch of garlic granules
1 free-range egg
4 fl oz (115ml/½ cup) Fish Brew (page 88)
a handful of Crunchy Crumbs (page 133)

Place the fish in a saucepan. Cover with water. Bring to the boil and simmer for ten minutes. Let it cool before skinning, flaking and removing all bones. Mix all the ingredients together except the Crunchy Crumbs. Put the mixture in a greased baking tin approximately 6 inches by 3 inches (15cm by 7.5cm) and bake at 350°F oven for one hour. Drop a handful of Crunchy Crumbs on top.

BOUBOULE BOUILLABAISSE

In 1897 Henri de Toulouse-Lautrec sketched a Bulldog called Bouboule which belonged to Mme Palmyre, who ran a lesbian restaurant called La Souris in Paris. Both dog and owner were known to have barks worse than their bites and the French nickname 'Bouboule' suited them both – meaning having a pudgy face and physique. However one thing they didn't have in common was Bouboule's dislike of women. It is said that he used to sneak under the tables and pee on the ladies' dresses!

½ teaspoon extra virgin olive oil
1 oz (30g) onion, chopped
½ clove garlic, crushed
1 tomato (3 oz/85g), peeled and chopped
½ oz (15g) watercress, chopped
10 fl oz (285ml/1¼ cups) water
2 oz (55g) cod fillet
2 oz (55g) haddock fillet
3 oz (85g) Crunchy Chunks (page 133)
1 oz (30g) Cheddar cheese, grated (optional)

Heat the olive oil in a pan. Add onion and garlic. Fry gently for five minutes. Stir in the tomato and watercress. Pour in the water and bring to the boil. Add the fish – flesh face-down, skin on top. Cover and simmer for 25 minutes. Lift the fish out. Skin, flake and discard any bones before returning the fish to the pan. Add Crunchy Chunks and Cheddar cheese.

Extra virgin olive oil contains the least amount of impurities of any oil because olives are easy to press and the oil can be obtained without heat or chemicals. Although low in linoleic acid, olive oil is high in oleic acid (80 per cent), making it one of the most digestible of edible oils. It is also a good source of calcium and iron and helps in the absorption of the fat-soluble vitamins – A, D, E, and K.

Hippocrates declared olive oil both a food and a medicine and to the Hebrews the olive was a symbol of prosperity.

FISH ON FRIDAY

Jeannie says: 'It's strange what one remembers from one's childhood, but one thing that sticks in my mind is "fish on Friday". My mother was a great traditionalist and not even the dogs were let off the hook!'

4 oz (115g) cod, whiting or coley
1 free-range egg
½ oz (15g) raw spinach, finely chopped
Crunchy Crumbs (page 133)

Place the fish in a pot. Cover with cold water. Bring to the boil. Simmer for ten minutes. Drain. Flake and remove any bones. Mix in the raw egg and spinach. Top with Crunchy Crumbs.

> There are conflicting views about whether to give dogs raw or cooked eggs. In their natural environment dogs would have eaten them raw and the Kemnitzer dogs never showed any ill-effects from having raw egg mixed with their Fish On Friday. It has been said that raw egg white contains an enzyme which destroys biotin, and if fed over a long period, this can result in a biotin deficiency, causing dry hair and flaky skin. However, it is fairly unlikely that one would feed a dog sufficiently large amounts of raw egg for this to occur.

OLD MOURNFUL'S PUB GRUB
MONDAY

'. . . I did have two regular companions during my stay in Fittleworth. One was a terrier mongrel, a skinny, wiry old thing with rusty tearmarks on his cheeks and a permanently dejected manner, who adopted me as a friend. Each day when lunch was over and I came through the darkened bar into the protestant hush of the afternoon, Old Mournful would be sitting there on the forecourt, his pink tongue beating in the heat, waiting, and when I walked past he would slowly rise and wander after me, like a guardian with a melancholy duty to perform.'

from *Waiting*
by Hugo Donnelly

2 free-range eggs, beaten
4 fl oz (115ml) goats' milk
1 tin (115g) Glenryck Pacific Pilchards in tomato sauce
3 oz (85g) wholemeal bread, sliced and cubed
a pinch of dill, chopped
2 oz (55g) Cheddar cheese, grated (optional)
1½ oz (45g) courgettes, sliced

Mix together the eggs, goats' milk, pilchards in tomato sauce, wholemeal bread, dill and Cheddar cheese. Line the base of a casserole dish with courgettes. Pour in the egg mixture. Bake at 350°F for one hour.

Dill helps the brain and the digestive system as well as giving vitality. It is also good for relieving flatulence and colic.

OLD MOURNFUL'S PUB GRUB
TUESDAY

5 oz (140g) potato, cubed
1 oz (30g) swede, peeled and sliced
1 oz (30g) carrot, peeled and sliced
4 oz (115g) cod fillet
1 teaspoon natural yoghurt
¼ teaspoon sesame seeds (optional)

Put the potato, swede and carrot in a pot. Cover with water. Bring to the boil and simmer for 10–15 minutes until the vegetables are tender. At the same time put the cod in a separate pot of boiling water and cook for ten minutes. Drain vegetables and mash with yoghurt. Drain, flake and de-bone the fish and add to the vegetable mash. Sprinkle the sesame seeds on top.

Sesame seeds are rich in vitamins and minerals – calcium, iron and protein. The god Yama in Hindu mythology blessed the sesame seed and in the East it is revered as a symbol of immortality.

OLD MOURNFUL'S PUB GRUB
WEDNESDAY

4 oz (115g) whiting
10–15 oz (285ml–430ml) Fish Brew (page 88)
½ oz (15g) watercress, finely chopped
1 oz (30g) broccoli florets, finely chopped
1 oz (30g) toasted oatbran

Place the whiting in a casserole dish. Pour over enough Fish Brew to cover the fish. Cover and bake in the oven for 25 minutes at 350°F. Allow to cool before skinning, flaking and de-boning. Meanwhile soak the watercress and broccoli in the hot Fish Brew for ten minutes. Drain. Mix the fish, watercress and broccoli together. Top with toasted oatbran.

OLD MOURNFUL'S PUB GRUB
THURSDAY

3 oz (85g) brown rice flakes
8 fl oz (230ml) Fish Brew (page 88)
4 oz (115g) haddock fillet
a pinch of tarragon, chopped
1 oz (30g) carrot, grated

Soak brown rice flakes in Fish Brew for 30 minutes. Gently grill the haddock for ten minutes – skin down. Turn over, remove skin and grill for a further five minutes. Allow to cool. Remove any bones and flake. Add tarragon, brown rice flakes and carrot.

OLD MOURNFUL'S PUB GRUB
FRIDAY

4 oz (115g/½ cup) broth mix – pearl barley, haricot beans, yellow split peas, green split peas, dried peas, split red lentils, brown long grain rice (yields 7 oz/200g when cooked)
2½ oz (70g) tuna in brine, drained
1 oz (30g) Crunchy Chunks (page 133)

Soak the broth mix in cold water for seven to ten hours. Drain. Boil in fresh water for ten minutes. Drain. Add the tuna and top with Crunchy Chunks.

Lentils which are seeds that have been dried, dehusked and sometimes split are rich in protein. If you want to give your dog less protein we suggest you halve the broth mix and treble up on Crunchy Chunks.

VEGETARIAN VICTUALS

'The chief food of the natives of Otaheite consists of vegetables. They have no tame animals, except poultry, hogs, and dogs, and these are not numerous. Captain Cook and his associates agreed that a South Sea dog was little inferior to a British lamb, which is probably occasioned by their being kept up, and fed solely upon vegetables.'

from *The Philosophy of Natural History*
by William Smellie

Can dogs be exclusively vegetarian? The answer is 'yes'. Although they are predominantly carnivores it is possible, with the right combinations of food, to have a vegetarian dog. Some hyperactive dogs with behavioural problems can actually improve on a vegetarian diet.

All animals (except humans who persist in consuming dairy products past adolescence) are naturally weaned at an early age. Cow products often cause different allergies and diseases because of lactose intolerance and should only be given in small amounts – if at all. Goats' and sheep's milk, cheeses and yoghurts are usually more easily tolerated and we recommend the use of free-range eggs as their battery counterparts contain little lecithin or methionine. We also advocate organic vegetables, and broccoli, cauliflower and cabbage stalks make excellent 'bones'. However, chemically treated raw carrots should be peeled first, but curiously my dogs showed no interest in carrots until I started to give them organic ones. There is of course no comparison in taste as they are so much sweeter.

All grated and chopped vegetables are an excellent source of roughage, but root vegetables such as turnips, swedes and potatoes should be cooked to make them more digestible.

If you are changing your dog from tins to a vegetarian diet do so slowly while the intestines get used to working properly again. An overnight change could make things a bit windy, although within a week this should stop!

Greengrocers often throw away imperfect vegetables. If you explain that they are for animals you may find your local supplier only too happy to give them to you instead of discarding them.

In order to have vegetarian dogs in optimum health one must rotate their menus. That way they receive the full range of vitamins and minerals in the correct ratios. Dr Pitcairn particularly advises the addition of extra vitamins A, C, E and D in the right amounts, according to the size of your dog.

Meat contains high fat levels but even more harmful are the levels of pesticides, hormones, antibiotics and chemicals in intensively-farmed animals today. It is also very hard to obtain wild meat so having a vegetarian dog fed on organic produce along with pulses, grains, nuts, seeds and fruit is a very healthy option.

Protein ratings (out of 100g)

Eggs 94
Milk 82 (pasteurised 70)
UHT 20
Cheese 70–75
Brown rice 70
Buckwheat 65
Broccoli and Brussels sprouts 60
Soya beans 61
Lentils 30
Corn 72
Cauliflower 60
Potato 60
Oats 65
Pumpkin seeds 60
Sesame seeds 55
Sunflower seeds 60
Peas 45
Chickpeas 45
Tofu 65
Walnuts 50
Wheat 60

BEEHIVE OR BEHAVE

An apple a day keeps the vet away!

1 large cooking apple
1 tablespoon clear honey

Peel and core the apple. Cut horizontally into rings. Place on foil in grill pan. Spread half the honey on the apple rings. Cook for three minutes under a hot grill. Turn over the rings and spread with remaining honey. Grill for another three minutes. Stack the rings in the shape of a beehive. Allow to cool before serving. Only serve if your dog behaves!

VEGGIE BREW

3 oz (85g) carrot, sliced
3 oz (85g) leek, sliced
4 oz (115g) swede, peeled and chopped
2 oz (55g) celery, chopped
3 oz (85g) turnip, peeled and chopped
3 oz (85g) potato, cubed
a pinch of sea salt
1 teaspoon Marmite (Yeast Extract)
30 fl oz (1½ pints UK/1¾ pints approx. USA) cold water

Put the vegetables, sea salt and Marmite in a saucepan with the cold water. Cover and bring to the boil. Simmer for 35 minutes. Strain off the liquid – Veggie Brew. Save the vegetables for:

VEGGIE STEW

2 oz (55g/⅓ cup) brown rice, cooked in boiling water for 30–35 minutes
4 oz (115g) vegetables, cooked
½ teaspoon Parmesan cheese, grated (optional)

Mix the brown rice and vegetables together. Sprinkle Parmesan cheese on top.

VEGGIE PÂTÉ

Purée the vegetables from Veggie Brew (page 104) and mix with Crunchy Chunks (page 133).

PONTO'S NUTTY ROAST

Alfred Jingle, the itinerant actor in Charles Dickens' *The Pickwick Papers*, credits his dog with amazing intelligence (perhaps more than his owner . . .):

'Ah, you should keep dogs – fine animals – sagacious creatures – dog of my own once – Pointer – surprising instinct – out shooting one day – entering enclosure – whistled – dogged stopped – whistled again – Ponto – no go; stock still – called him – Ponto, Ponto – wouldn't move – dog transfixed – staring at a board – looked up, saw an inscription – "Gamekeeper has orders to shoot all dogs found in this enclosure" – wouldn't pass it – wonderful dog – valuable dog that – very.'

from *The Pickwick Papers*
by Charles Dickens

½ clove garlic, crushed
1 oz (30g) onion, peeled and chopped
1 oz (30g) mushrooms, chopped
1 oz (30g) tomato, chopped
1 teaspoon parsley, chopped
1½ teaspoons extra virgin olive oil
4 oz (115g) mixed nuts* (walnuts, almonds and Brazil nuts), chopped
4 oz (115g) oatmeal with bran
1 free-range egg, beaten
9 fl oz (255ml/½ pint approx. USA) Veggie Brew (page 104)

Fry the garlic, onion, mushrooms, tomato and parsley in olive oil for five minutes. Mix together the nuts and oatmeal. Add the vegetables, egg and Veggie Brew. Put the mixture in a small loaf tin and bake in the oven at 350°F for 35 minutes.

*You can use any mixture of nuts provided they don't include peanuts. Some dogs can have an allergic reaction to peanuts – in fact Roscoe, the Dobermann, raided the sack of birds' peanuts and ended up very poorly at the vet's.

JASPER'S CORNY CARROTS

Jasper was the name of the Cocker Spaniel belonging to Maxim de Winter in Daphne du Maurier's novel *Rebecca*.

'Jasper lapped noisily at his drinking bowl below the stairs, the sound echoing in the great stone hall.'

from *Rebecca*
by Daphne du Maurier

3 oz (85g) carrots, grated
5 oz (140g) creamed sweetcorn
2 oz (55g/½ cup) macaroni, cooked in boiling water for 18–20 minutes

Mix all the ingredients together and heat gently.

The Native American Indians and Mexicans worshipped corn and believed it to hold the powers of fertility. It has such a high nutritional value that they could exist solely on corn for months at a time. Corn is an excellent tonic for glandular problems as well as aiding in the growth of healthy hair and teeth. Dogs, as well as cats, like tinned sweetcorn, especially the creamed variety. Corn, like pineapple, does not lose its vitamins in the canning process.

KEMKIBBLE

4 oz (115g) self-raising wholemeal flour
4 oz (115g) brown rice flour
1 oz (30g) organic pinhead oats
1 oz (30g) rye flakes
1 oz (30g) barley flakes
1 oz (30g) toasted oatbran
2 oz (55g) dried skimmed milk
1 tablespoon bonemeal
1 tablespoon green nori flakes
10 fl oz (285ml) water
3 tablespoons unrefined sesame oil
1 tablespoon tamari soy sauce
1 free-range egg, beaten

Mix together the wholemeal flour, brown rice flour, pinhead oats, rye flakes, barley flakes, toasted oatbran, dried skimmed milk and bonemeal. Add the water. In a separate bowl combine the sesame oil, tamari soy sauce and the egg. Add this to the rest of the ingredients. Pour batter, about ½ inch thick, on to a greased baking tray. Bake at 350°F for 50 minutes. Once it is cool, crumble. Put the KemKibble crumbs on a baking tray and cook in the oven at 300°F for 45 minutes. For extra-crunchy KemKibble, turn off the oven and let the kibble dry out in the oven for five to seven hours.

POLYBE POTATO PIE

Polybe was a Mallorcan Hound that belonged to Gertrude Stein and Alice B Toklas, named after the articles signed 'Polybe' in *Figaro*. Polybe featured in many of Gertrude Stein's plays and he was remembered for having a passion for smelling roses!

6 oz (170g) potatoes, peeled and thinly sliced
1 oz (30g) carrot, grated
1 oz (30g) onion, peeled and chopped
1 free-range egg, beaten
10 fl oz (285ml) Veggie Brew (page 104)

Mix the carrot and onion together. Layer, alternately, the potato slices and the carrot/onion mixture in a small loaf tin starting and finishing with the potato. Add the egg to the Veggie Brew and pour over the vegetables. Bake covered in the oven at 400°F for one hour.

PINPIN'S PUMPKIN PIE

Émile Zola, the French novelist, had a black Pomeranian called Sir Hector Pinpin, who couldn't live without his master. In 1898, Émile Zola was sentenced to prison in connection with the Dreyfus case. However, he escaped to England for a year, but by the time he returned to Paris heralded as a hero, poor Pinpin had died from grief.

16 oz (455g) pumpkin
1 oz (30g) soya margarine
a pinch of nutmeg
1 oz (30g) Parmesan cheese, grated (optional)
1 oz (30g) fresh wholemeal breadcrumbs

Peel the pumpkin, cut in half, remove seeds and dice. Put the pumpkin pieces in a pot, cover with water and boil for 15 minutes. Drain. Melt margarine in a frying pan, add the pumpkin and nutmeg. Mix well. Place the pumpkin in a greased baking dish. Mix together the Parmesan cheese and breadcrumbs and sprinkle on top. Bake at 400°F until browned on top.

Don't throw away the pumpkin seeds if you have a bitch in season. Raw minced pumpkin seeds will do her good. In addition canned pumpkin has been known to help if your dog is suffering from constipation. It is an excellent source of fibre and by mixing a tablespoon with your dog's food for a few days you are more than likely to see an improvement.

BROCCOLI AU BOUVIER DES FLANDRES

Bouvier des Flandres is of European origin from an area near Brussels in Belgium. This breed is believed to have descended from the griffon, a coarse-haired terrier-like dog. It was used as a cattle-droving dog until modern farming methods made it redundant. With its herding instinct the Bouvier des Flandres is great for rounding up children . . .

3 oz (85g) broccoli, cooked
2 oz (55g) split peas, cooked
1 free-range egg, hard-boiled
2 oz (55g) wholemeal spaghetti, cooked in boiling water with ½ teaspoon of Marmite or Yeast Extract for eight to ten minutes
1 teaspoon sunflower seeds

Mix all the ingredients together

TAMING TABOULEH

'A hound it was, an enormous coal-black hound, but not such a hound as mortal eyes have ever seen. Fire burst from its open mouth, its eyes glowed with a smouldering glare, its muzzle and hackles and dewlap were outlined in flickering flame. Never in the delirious dream of a disordered brain could anything more savage, more appalling, more hellish, be conceived than that dark form and savage face which broke upon us out of the wall of fog.'

from *The Hound of the Baskervilles*
by Arthur Conan Doyle

A gentle meal like this could help to tame an aggressive dog!

2 oz (55g) bulghur wheat, soaked in boiling water for 30 minutes
1 tablespoon onion, chopped
1 oz (30g) cucumber, finely diced
½ tomato, finely chopped
1 oz (30g) bean sprouts, soaked in cold water for ten minutes
1 oz (30g) goats' cheese, crumbled
¼ teaspoon parsley, chopped
¼ teaspoon mint, chopped
½ teaspoon lemon juice

Mix all the ingredients together.

VEGAN VARIATIONS

'The act of putting into your mouth what the earth has grown is perhaps your most direct interaction with the earth.'

from *Diet For A Small Planet*
by Frances Moore Lappé

A dog can only be a healthy vegan if its owner acquires sufficient knowledge of the various pulses, grains, vegetables and fruits needed to maintain the correct nutritional balance. Vegans do not eat meat, poultry, fish, eggs or dairy products; so it is important to be aware of the protein ratings in the other foods, e.g.: (out of 100g) – brown rice 70; buckwheat 65; broccoli and Brussels sprouts 60; soya beans 61; lentils 30; corn 72; cauliflower 60; potato 60; oats 65; pumpkin seeds 60; sesame seeds 55; sunflower seeds 60; peas 45; chickpeas 45; tofu 65; walnuts 50 and wheat 60.

The fatty acids necessary to maintain a beautiful coat come from nuts and seeds such as safflower, sunflower, corn and soya oils. Equally there is no need for a vitamin deficiency as vitamin A is found in carrots, pumpkins, tomatoes and greens. Vitamin B is found in nuts, oats, lentils, Marmite, potatoes, dried fruit, tamari, miso, and the sea vegetables hijiki, nori and wakame. Calcium and iron are obtainable from seeds, nuts, carob, beans, tofu, parsley, sea vegetables and oatmeal.

If by any chance your dog has difficulty in tolerating bean products, alternatives to soya milk are oat milk or rice dream. Oat milk is made from water, oats and rapeseed oil and rice dream contains filtered water, organic brown rice, expeller pressed high oleic safflower oil and a tiny amount of sea salt.

Fortunately most dogs like fruit, which are a valuable source of vitamin C. My first Dobermann, Blue, would eat cherries and spit out the stones while Jeannie's Springer Spaniel, Brandy, would pick blackberries directly from the bush! All our dogs have loved apples, and I do believe that an apple a day combined with a good vitamin/mineral supplement keeps the vet away.

'6 August 1844
Here is Flush, rejoicing like Bacchus himself, among the grapes! eating one grape after another, with exceeding complacency, shown by swingings of the tail. "Very good grapes, indeed!"'

from *Letters of Elizabeth Barrett Browning to Mary Russell Mitford*, edited by Meredith B. Raymond and Mary Rose Sullivan

MUTT'S MUSHROOM MEDLEY

Mutt was the name of the charming little mongrel who was the star of Charlie Chaplin's film *A Dog's Life*.

3 oz (85g) mushrooms, chopped
½ oz (15g) green pepper, chopped
1 oz (30g) courgette, chopped
a pinch of thyme, chopped
1 teaspoon unrefined sunflower oil
3 oz (85g/½ cup) brown rice, cooked in boiling water for 30–35 minutes
1 teaspoon walnuts, finely chopped

Sauté the mushrooms, pepper, courgette and thyme in sunflower oil for five minutes. Add brown rice and walnuts.

BULGHUR FOR A PIT BULL TERRIER

Can you imagine being arrested on account of your looks or ancestry, being put behind bars at a secret location, friends and relations having to pay up to £300 to visit you, having a death sentence or life imprisonment hanging over you for a crime you have never committed? It is hard to believe that this has been happening in the UK since the Dangerous Dogs Act 1991 came into force. Naturally there are some valid cases but it is the innocent victims and their owners who are suffering. So if you are a Pit Bull Terrier, Japanese Tosa, Dogo Argentino or a Fila Braziliero or a cross of these breeds, don't even think of trying to come to the UK!

4 oz (115g) tofu
¼ teaspoon Kikkoman naturally brewed soy sauce
7 fl oz (200ml) Veggie Brew (page 104)
2½ oz (70g/½ cup) bulghur wheat, soaked in boiling water for 30 minutes
1 oz (30g) onion, chopped
½ clove garlic, crushed
4 oz (115g) carrot, sliced
1 cooking apple, peeled, cored and chopped
1 oz (30g) sultanas

Put the tofu, soy sauce and Veggie Brew in a blender and mix until smooth. Mix all the other ingredients together and add the liquid. Put in a casserole dish and bake for 40 minutes at 350°F. There should be enough for a couple of meals or more, depending on how hungry your dog is.

LAP IT UP LASSI

Lassi is a traditional Indian yoghurt drink.

10 fl oz (285ml) vegan yoghurt
30 fl oz (865ml) natural spring water
1 teaspoon honey

Mix the yoghurt, water and honey in a blender. Work until smooth.

FANNY'S FRY-UP

In Thomas Hardy's *Far From The Madding Crowd* when Fanny is homeless and in a weakened state a 'Newfoundland, mastiff, bloodhound, or what not, it was impossible to say' befriends her and leads her to safety.

'The animal, who was as homeless as she, respectfully withdrew a step or two when the woman moved, and, seeing that she did not repulse him, he licked her hand again.'

2 teaspoons unrefined sunflower oil
4 oz (115g) tofu, crumbled
1 teaspoon parsley, chopped
2 oz (55g) cabbage, shredded
1 teaspoon watercress, chopped
¼ teaspoon Marmite and 1 tablespoon boiling water
1 teaspoon green nori flakes
3 oz (85g) Crunchy Chunks (page 133)

Fry the tofu, parsley, cabbage and watercress in sunflower oil for three minutes. Add Marmite and water mixed, and cook for another five minutes. Sprinkle on the nori flakes. Toss in Crunchy Chunks and mix well.

LITE LUNCHES

'Asking a working writer what he thinks about critics is like asking a lamp-post how it feels about dogs.'
from *The Sunday Times* Magazine (16 Oct 1977)
by Christopher Hampton

3 oz (85g) broccoli florets, chopped
3 oz (85g) Crunchy Crumbs (page 133)
1 teaspoon bonemeal
1 tablespoon pumpkin seeds, ground

Mix all the ingredients together.

or

2 oz (55g) bean sprouts, soaked in cold water for ten minutes
2 oz (55g/⅓ cup) bulghur wheat, soaked in boiling water for 30 minutes
1 oz (30g) carrot, grated
1 teaspoon sunflower seeds or pine kernels, ground

Mix all the ingredients together.

or

2 oz (55g/⅓ cup) bulghur wheat, soaked in boiling water for 30 minutes
1 oz (30g) beetroot, cooked and chopped
1 stick of celery, chopped
1 teaspoon wakame, soaked in cold water for ten minutes

Mix all the ingredients together.

BUFFY BURGERS

'Good, darling. Then I'll expect you. *(Pause)*
Yes, the dogs will be fine – yes! Yes, of course they'll be fed. *(Pause)*
Estelle! What do you think I am? I know what to feed a Gaddam Dog! *(Pause)*
Dog food, for God's sake! Any fool can feed a dog! What do you think I'm going to feed them? Chicken food? A bit of caviar and the rest of the champagne?
You're absolutely mad! I did not feed poor little Buffy alcohol! You're making a mountain over the fact that the poor thing liked a spot of brandy now and then! *(Listening)*
Estelle, the dog was not a candidate for AA, and I will not have Robert fix the dinners!'

from the play *Tallulah!*
by Sandra Ryan Heyward

1 oz (30g/½ cup) dried soya mince (soaked in boiling water for 10 minutes)
1 oz (30g/⅓ cup) oats with bran
1 oz (30g/⅓ cup) rye flakes
1 teaspoon green nori flakes
1 teaspoon natural wheatgerm
1 oz (30g) carrot, grated
2 tablespoons tomato juice

Squeeze out any excess water in the soya mince. Mix together well the soya mince, oats with bran, rye flakes and wheatgerm. Form into two burgers and place them on a greased baking tray. Bake in the oven at 350°F for 40 minutes, turning them over after 20 minutes. Pour the tomato juice over the burgers and serve with grated carrot.

VEGAN CRUMBLE

12 oz (340g/3 cups) porridge oats with bran
6 oz (170g/1½ cups)self-raising wholemeal flour
1 teaspoon brewer's yeast
2 oz (55g) raisins
2 oz (55g) mixed nuts (walnuts, almonds and Brazil nuts), chopped
5 oz (140g) tofu, blended
6 fl oz (170g) unrefined grapeseed oil
1 tablespoon vanilla
3 oz (85g) honey

Mix the oats, flour, brewer's yeast, raisins and nuts together in a large bowl. In a smaller bowl mix the tofu, grapeseed oil, vanilla and honey. Then combine all the ingredients together in the large bowl and mix well. Spread on a greased baking tray and bake in the oven at 350°F for 20 minutes. Use sparingly as a topping.

GRAINS FOR GELERT

'Ah, what was then Llewelyn's pain,
For now the truth was clear:
His gallant hound the wolf had slain,
To save Llewelyn's heir.'

from *Beth-Gelert*
by W.R. Spencer

A Welsh legend dating back to the 13th century tells us of Prince Llewelyn who went off to fight the English leaving his Irish Wolfhound, Gelert, to guard his baby. When Llewelyn returned he found his dog's mouth dripping with blood and immediately assumed that Gelert had ravaged his son. In his fury he plunged his sword into Gelert. Moments later he heard the faint cries of his baby and discovered him alive near the mangled remains of a huge wolf. Instantly Llewelyn realized his dreadful mistake – Gelert had killed the wolf to save his son. But it was too late. Gelert only managed to lick his master's hand gently before expiring.

5 oz (140g) Shipton's 5 Cereals Blend – malted wheat flakes, barley flakes, sunflower seeds, millet and oats
6 fl oz (170ml) organic apple juice

Soak the 5 Cereals Blend in the apple juice for at least 30 minutes, or longer if your dog prefers a moister texture.

MACROBIOTIC MORSELS

'I love best to have each thing in its season only, and enjoy doing without it at all other times.'

Henry Thoreau

The macrobiotic diet has often been regarded as a fad by the Western world. However, it is a diet very much about preventative medicine, which has cured many animals of serious diseases. It is the reverse of the modern trend towards chemicals, refinement and large-scale commerce and requires a positive change in diet. Degenerative diseases such as heart disorders, cancer, arthritis, allergies and diabetes are very common today and may improve on a diet of whole grains, seeds, nuts, vegetables and fruit with meat, dairy foods and sugar being kept to a minimum. Apart from the aforementioned diseases, if a dog with hyperactive or behavioural problems is changed from canned foods to a macrobiotic diet there is usually a significant improvement in its demeanour.

Yin and Yang, the Oriental philosophy, is behind the macrobiotic diet – 'macros' in Greek meaning great and 'bios' life, thus the great study of life – and is about achieving the correct balance of foods.

The macrobiotic philosophy also encourages local foods to be eaten as available each season. This diet is excellent for keeping healthy dogs in good condition. However it should not be given to dogs with heart, kidney or thyroid problems as the seaweeds and tahini have a high sodium content.

PUTTING A MEAL TOGETHER

Soup, approximately 5 per cent
Grains, 50 per cent or more
Legumes and seeds, more or less 10 per cent
Vegetables and sea vegetables, about 25 per cent
Animal-quality food, 5 per cent or no more than 10 per cent
Seasoning
Desserts, fruits and nuts, a moderate 5 per cent
Drinks

from *The Practically Macrobiotic Cookbook*
by Keith Michell

This is a guide to balancing the type of food used in a macrobiotic meal. If you do want to include meat (animal-quality food), use it 'as a condiment'. George Ohsawa who is responsible for introducing the macrobiotic way of life to the Western world believes: 'If it can protest or run away – don't eat it!' Clearly he didn't have dogs in mind when he said that . . .

MORNING MUSE

2 oz (55g/½ cup) brown rice, cooked in boiling water for 30–35 minutes
1 teaspoon green nori flakes
3 dates, pitted and chopped
1 teaspoon sunflower seeds

Mix all the ingredients together.

DASHING GOOD TEA

Queen Victoria owned many dogs in her lifetime, including Collies, Dachshunds, Greyhounds, Pomeranians, a Pekinese and a Tibetan Mastiff, but her first was a Spaniel called Dash.

9 January 1839
I sent for Dashy, who Lord [Melbourne] accused of having crooked legs, which I wouldn't allow! We put him on the table and he was very much petted and admired by Lord M, who was so funny about him! We gave him tea and Lord M said, 'I wonder if lapping is a pleasant sensation,' – for that is a thing we had never felt.

from *More Leaves from the Journal of a Life in the Highlands*
by Queen Victoria

2 strips of kombu
20 fl oz (570ml) water
1 teaspoon tamari soy sauce

Put the kombu and water in a saucepan. Bring to the boil and simmer for 25 minutes. Take out the kombu and add tamari soy sauce. Allow to cool before serving.

(Dashi is a macrobiotic broth made with kombu!)

When Dash died in 1840, Queen Victoria had the following epitaph engraved on his tombstone at Adelaide Lodge:

'His attachment was without selfishness
His playfulness without malice
His fidelity without deceit
Reader, if you would live beloved and die regretted, profit by the example of Dash.'

BARNEY'S BARLEY STEW

'This is the dog,
That worried the cat,
That killed the rat,
That ate the malt
That lay in the house
that Jack built.'

The House That Jack Built
Traditional Nursery Rhyme

Jeannie says: 'Barney Blundell was a mischievous yellow Labrador Retriever who belonged to my godparents and was always in trouble. He stole sausages from the local butcher, wellington boots from neighbours' porches and if the milkman left a carton of cream on anyone's doorstep within the vicinity, Barney always got to it first on one of his early morning raids. Nobody was immune from Barney's antics – he even stole a policeman's hat and ran down the beach and dropped it in the sea. But Toffee Mabey, a yappy French Bulldog/Yorkshire Terrier cross, came off worst. Toffee annoyed Barney so much so that one day he picked him up by the scruff of his neck, carried him into the sea and dunked him three or four times. We were to discover shortly afterwards that Toffee had swallowed what seemed like gallons of sea water . . .!'

1 oz (30g) carrot, grated
1 oz (30g) onion, chopped
2 oz (55g) cabbage, shredded
1 teaspoon unrefined sunflower oil
2 oz (55g) pearl barley, cooked in boiling water for 30 minutes

Fry the carrot, onion and cabbage in the sunflower oil for five minutes. Add the pearl barley.

A MORSEL FOR BULLSEYE

Bill Sikes, the villain in Charles Dickens' *Oliver Twist*, had a Bull Terrier called Bullseye.

'There was a fire in the tap-room, and some country-labourers were drinking before it. They made room for the stranger, but he sat down in the farthest corner, and ate and drank alone, or rather with his dog, to whom he cast a morsel of food from time to time.'

from *Oliver Twist*
by Charles Dickens

8 oz (230g) tofu, mashed
1 tablespoon parsley, chopped
1 oz (30g) onion, chopped
½ clove garlic, crushed
1 tablespoon tamari soy sauce
1 oz (30g) oatbran and wheatgerm
3 oz (85g) cabbage, shredded

Mix all the ingredients together except the cabbage. Place the mixture in a small loaf tin and bake in the oven for 1 hour at 350°F. Remove the contents from the tin, break the tofu mixture into small portions and mix with the cabbage.

NIPPER NOSH

If your dog appears to be suffering from boredom or depression, especially if you are out for the greater part of the day (when your dog would like to hear his owner's voice), music can ease the situation. Dogs particularly like classical music and opera. Alternatively you could put on an animal video as you leave the house – it will help your pet relax and not feel so lonely.

3 oz (85g) bulghur wheat, soaked in boiling water for 30 minutes
1 stick of celery, chopped
3 oz (85g) carrot, thinly sliced
2 oz (55g) mushrooms, chopped
4 oz (115g) tofu
6 fl oz (170ml) Dashing Good Tea (page 130)

Mix together the bulghur wheat, celery, carrot and mushrooms and place in a casserole dish. Put the tofu and Dashing Good Tea in a blender. When it's smooth, pour over the ingredients in the casserole dish. Bake in the oven at 350°F for 30 minutes.

COLOURFUL CABBAGE

'Folks either must avoid temptation
Or face my nasal accusation.'

from *The Bloodhound*
by Thomas Hood

2 oz (55g/⅓ cup) brown rice, cooked in boiling water for 30–35 minutes
4 oz (115g) red cabbage, shredded
1 apple, cored and chopped
1 tablespoon onion, chopped
¼ teaspoon mint, chopped

Mix all the ingredients together.

There are over forty varieties of mint – the most popular being spearmint (otherwise known as common garden mint). Mint helps digestion and its aroma enhances both man and dog's appetite. Mint has been grown for centuries and we learn from Pliny that the Romans particularly fancied this herb: 'The smell of Mint does stir up the minde . . . It is applied with salt to the bitings of mad dogs.'

Raw cabbage is particularly good for a dog suffering from anaemia.

SCHNAUZER SPINACH

In David Marr's book, *Life of Patrick White* we learn that people who love Schnauzers say they 'are demanding, intelligent and so loyal that they haunt their owners' footsteps like pepper-and-salt ghosts'. P.V.M. White and E.G. Lascaris were responsible for reintroducing the Schnauzer to Australia in the late '40s, where their particular strain of breed became noted at the Royal Easter Show held annually in Sydney.

4 oz (115g) spinach, steamed
¼ teaspoon extra virgin olive oil
2 oz (55g/⅓ cup) brown rice, cooked in boiling water for 30–35 minutes
1 tablespoon fresh wholemeal breadcrumbs
1 tablespoon natural wheatgerm
1 fl oz (30ml) Veggie Brew (page 104)

Mix the spinach, olive oil and brown rice together and put in a casserole dish. Mix together the breadcrumbs and wheatgerm and put on top of the spinach/rice mixture. Pour the Veggie Brew over the contents of the casserole dish and bake for 25 minutes at 350°F.

Your dog might appreciate a little Parmesan cheese sprinkled on top before baking.

CRUNCHY CRUMBS

Take any amount of stale brown bread. Rub into breadcrumbs, not necessarily super-fine. Sprinkle the breadcrumbs on a large baking tray and bake in the oven for 30 minutes at 300°F. Crunchy Crumbs make a delicious topping for any meal and to vary them you can add ground nuts (Brazil nuts, hazelnuts etc.) or seeds (pumpkin, poppy, sunflower, etc.)

CRUNCHY CHUNKS

Slice any amount of wholemeal bread and cut into medium-sized chunks. Put on a baking tray and bake in the oven at 300°F for 45 minutes till crisp. You can add a bit of grated cheese to Crunchy Chunks to give your dog a different topping for his usual meal.

DRINK OR TREAT

'He who drinks a little too much drinks much too much.'

Proverb

'Toto was not grey; he was a little black dog, with long silky hair and small black eyes that twinkled merrily on either side of his funny, wee nose.
. . . and taking a pail from the shelf, she carried it down to the little brook and filled it with clear, sparkling water . . . having helped herself and Toto to a drink of the cool, clear water, she set about making ready for the journey to the City of Emeralds.'

from *The Wizard of Oz*
by L. Frank Baum

Have you ever questioned what is actually coming out of your taps? The mineral content in water varies from region to region and some areas treat their water supply with chemicals. When Bob Mann, a parrot breeder near Peterborough, found his baby parrots were all dying he did a thorough investigation and traced the problem to his local reservoir. In the hot summer the nitrates, and chlorides had risen far above the acceptable levels and had poisoned the baby parrots. Because of the amount of chlorine and fluoride in most tap water, we advocate bottled or filtered water. Make sure the bottled water you purchase has been purified by a natural method. Also some plastic bottles can have an adverse effect on health, so whenever possible buy water in glass bottles. This too has the added advantage that they can be recycled.

	Chloride	Nitrate	Sodium
Ballygowan	28.0	9.0	15.0
Buxton	42.0	0.1	24.0
Caledonian	8.0	2.0	6.8
Chiltern Hills	15.0	5.0	8.0
Evian	4.5	3.8	5.0
Highland Spring	7.5	1.0	6.0
Strathmore	125.0	5.0	46.0
Vittel	–	0.6	7.3
Volvic	8.4	6.3	9.4
Welsh Mineral Water	12.0	1.3	5.0

If you can afford bottled water, do check the contents and make sure it has the lowest possible amount of chlorides, nitrates and sodium. An excessive amount of sodium in a dog's diet is bad for animals with a heart condition or diabetes and can also lead to hypertension. If you haven't already studied a typical analysis of bottled water, you will be amazed at the differences between the brands.

Throughout the day a dog loses water through panting, urine and faeces, depending on how much exercise it has and the climate. It is essential that this water be replaced. However, it is also important to keep an eye on how much water your dog drinks, because an excessive amount can indicate the early signs of a disease.
The following is a guideline:

Dog's Weight	**Daily Water Requirement** (from various sources, i.e. moisture contained in food)
30–50 pounds	1–1½ pints
70–90 pounds	2–3 pints

Some people may have been guilty of offering their dogs a taste of alcohol for fun, but it can be harmful and is not advised. An exception for dogs in distress would be neat Bach's Rescue Remedy which contains brandy.

> 'Last week was one of sadness. Charley dog died full of years but leaving a jagged hole nevertheless. He died of what would probably be called cirrhosis in a human. This degeneration is usually ascribed to indulgence in alcohol. But Charley did not drink, or if he did he was very secret about it.'
>
> from *Last Days*, a letter to D.E.S. Montgomery, April 1963
> by John Steinbeck

It is best not to get in the habit of feeding your dog between meals and to resist the pleading eyes at the dinner table. If you have leftovers from your meal, provided they are not highly seasoned, spicy or sugary, keep them for your dog's next meal.

> 'Jesus replied, "It is not right to take the children's bread and throw it to the dogs." "True, sir," she answered; "and yet the dogs eat the scraps that fall from their masters' table."'
>
> from *The New English Bible: New Testament*
> Matthew 15, verses 26 and 27

Treats should be used only as a reward for good behaviour and then given sparingly – as food and over-indulgence can lead to obesity and all the ensuing problems. Raw carrots, apples, grapes, cucumber and even dried fruits make a healthy alternative, and have you tried air-popped popcorn?

Although most dogs will jump at the chance of eating chocolate, it contains the stimulant theobromine which, if given to dogs in large quantities, can act as a poison. Baking chocolate has nearly nine times the amount of theobromine as milk chocolate. This is not to say don't ever give your dog chocolate, but try substituting with carob-based treats. Carob looks like and tastes like chocolate but has no refined sugar or caffeine.

'She gave him rich dainties
Whenever he fed,
And erected a monument
When he was dead.'

from *Old Mother Hubbard and Her Dog*
Traditional Nursery Rhyme

L'EAU GLACÉ

Chacun à son goût!

1 bowl of natural spring water (preferably bottled in France!)
2 ice cubes
squeeze of lemon juice

Combine all the ingredients in a drinking bowl. Allow the ice to melt. Serve.

On a more serious note, if your dog is suffering from severe dehydration try offering him an ice cube to suck before he consumes vast quantities of liquid which could make him sick.

Giving a puppy an ice cube to chew on will help ease the pain of teething.

ALBUMEN WATER

1 free-range egg
1 teaspoon glucose powder
water

Boil some water and let it cool. Beat the egg white together with the glucose powder and a tablespoon of water.

If your dog suffers from travel sickness this concoction could help ease the problem.

HONEY WATER

20 fl oz (570ml/2½ cups) water
1 tablespoon honey

Boil the water, stir in the honey. Let it cool. Serve.

If you are feeding your dog a dry-mixer all-in-one food the addition of honey water will make it far more palatable and nutritious. Honey is easily digested and goes straight into the bloodstream because it has already been pre-digested by bees and is therefore a quick source of energy. If your dog is known to suffer from hypoglycaemia (low blood sugar), an emergency measure could be to rub honey on its gums. Honey is also a good tonic for heart and nervous conditions.

BARLEY WATER

20 fl oz (570ml/2½ cups) water
1 tablespoon pearl barley

Boil the water, add the pearl barley and simmer for 25 minutes. Allow to cool before straining off the liquid. Serve.

This drink is rich in magnesium and helps to purify the blood so it is an excellent remedy if your dog is suffering from a skin complaint or rheumatism. If your dog has a kidney disease or is showing signs of not digesting its food properly (such as severe diarrhoea and a decrease in weight) barley water should be its only intake of liquid. To make it a bit more appetising one can add honey (1 tablespoon per pint of liquid.)

OLD YELLER OAT MILK

Jeannie says: 'Part of growing up in the States was being introduced at an early age to *Old Yeller* by Fred Gipson, the first moving book about a dog that really captured one's imagination and brought emotions to the surface. I can still see Mrs Heinisch, our teacher, in tears at the end of the book every time she read it to her class of eight-year-olds.'

4 oz (115g) oats
40 fl oz water
a pinch of salt
1 tablespoon honey or maple syrup
1 teaspoon unrefined grapeseed oil

Heat the water to near-boiling and pour over the oats. Let this mixture stand overnight. Strain off the liquid. Add a pinch of salt, the honey and grapeseed oil to the 'oat milk'. Reheat till lukewarm.

Oats should be an important ingredient in every dog's diet, particularly stud dogs and brood bitches. This grain provides a good source of iron and at the same time acts as an excellent agent for cleansing the intestines. Oats can be used as a tonic for dogs suffering from a nervous condition. This drink would be beneficial to any dog feeling a little under-the-weather.

TIPPY DAWS DOG BISCUITS

1 lb (455g/4 cups) Singleton stoneground wholemeal flour*
9 oz (255g/1¾ cups) bulghur wheat
3 oz (85g/1 cup) oats with bran
3 oz (85g/1¼ cups) dried skimmed milk
2 tablespoons dried parsley
½ teaspoon garlic granules
1½ teaspoons dried yeast
12 fl oz (340ml/1½ cups) Meaty Brew, Fish Brew or Veggie Brew (pages 73, 88, 104)
1 free-range egg, beaten

Mix all the dry ingredients together, add the brew and egg. Knead and roll out to ¼ or ½ of an inch, depending on the size of dog. Using a dog-shaped cutter make the biscuits and place on a floured baking tray. Bake at 300°F for 35–40 minutes. Cool on a rack, or if you want the biscuits extra-hard, turn the oven off and let them dry out on the baking tray in the oven for five to seven hours.

*Singleton stoneground wholemeal flour is produced in the Lurgashall Mill which is now sited at the Weald and Downland Museum in Singleton, West Sussex.

NOBLE BIRTHDAY CAKE

'My favourite collie Noble is always downstairs when we take our meals, and was so good, Brown making him lie on a chair or couch, and he never attempted to come down without permission, and even held a piece of cake in his mouth without eating it, till told he might.'

from *More Leaves from the Journal of a Life in the Highlands*
by Queen Victoria

1 teaspoon extra virgin olive oil
3 oz (85g) chicken mince
½ oz (15g) onion, chopped
½ teaspoon garlic granules
½ teaspoon green nori flakes
2 oz (55g) superfine self-raising wholemeal flour
2 oz (55g) soya margarine
1 teaspoon honey
1 free-range egg, beaten

Fry the chicken mince, onion and garlic granules in the olive oil for six to eight minutes, stirring occasionally. Combine with the nori flakes, wholemeal flour, soya margarine, honey and egg. Place the mixture in a baking tin approximately 6 inches by 3 inches (15cm by 7.5cm) and cook in the oven at 360°F for 25 minutes.

NOBLE LIVER ICING

½ teaspoon unrefined sesame oil
1 teaspoon onion, chopped
3 oz (85g) chicken livers, chopped
a pinch of rosemary, chopped
1 tablespoon natural Greek-style yoghurt

Fry the onion, chicken livers and rosemary in the sesame oil for six to eight minutes, stirring occasionally. Put all the ingredients into a blender and combine until you have a smooth paste. Spread the Noble Liver Icing on the top of the Noble Birthday Cake (page 142). Invite some of your dog's best pals round to share this delicious concoction.

LIVER TRAINING TREATS

16 oz (455g) liver
3 cloves garlic, crushed

Cut the liver into medium-sized pieces (they shrink during cooking). Mix with crushed garlic cloves. Place in a greased baking dish. Cover and bake in the oven at 325°F for two hours. Allow them to cool and harden.

These make a welcome and healthy reward for dogs in training – they love them and will do virtually anything for you in order to get one!

SUGAR-FREE SHAG SHAPES

Virginia Woolf had a Skye Terrier called Shag, who knew better than to accept any sugar in his diet:

'The solitary occasion when he [Shag] found it necessary to inflict marks of his displeasure on human flesh was once when a visitor rashly tried to treat him as an ordinary pet-dog and tempted him with sugar and called him "out of his name" by the contemptible lap-dog title of "Fido".'

from *On a Faithful Friend* (1904)
by Virginia Woolf

16 oz (455g) Shipton's organic light rye flour
12 oz (340g) Shipton's 5 Cereals Blend – malted wheat flakes, barley flakes, sunflower seeds, millet and oats or similar mix
3 oz (85g) dried milk powder
3 oz (85g) chicken livers, chopped
3 oz (85g) chicken, minced
2 teaspoons green nori flakes
1 teaspoon cold-pressed virgin sunflower oil
8 oz (230ml) Meaty Brew – made with chicken bones (page 73)
1 free-range egg, beaten
1 tablespoon unrefined sesame oil
1 tablespoon fresh parsley, chopped

Mix together the rye flour, 5 Cereals Blend and milk powder. Fry the chicken livers, chicken and nori flakes in the sunflower oil for 10–12 minutes. Put the fried chicken livers, chicken and nori flakes in a blender with the Meaty Brew, egg, sesame oil and parsley.

Combine until you have a smooth consistency. Add this to the dry ingredients and mix well until you have a stiff dough. Roll out on a floured board to approximately ¼ inch thick. Using a dog-bone shape cutter, make as many shapes as you can. Place them on a baking tray and cook in the oven at 350°F for 30 minutes. Cool on a rack or if you want extra-hard Shag Shapes, turn the oven off and allow them to dry out for five to seven hours in the oven.

Sugar-Free Shag Shapes *must* be stored in a refrigerator.

TASTERS' TITBITS

14 oz (400g) Singleton stoneground wholemeal flour
2 oz (55g) brown rice flour
4 oz (115g) bulghur wheat
3 oz (85g) oats with bran
1 oz (30g) rye flakes
1 oz (30g) toasted oatbran
1 oz (30g) barley flakes
1 oz (30g) corn meal
1 oz (30g) natural wheatgerm
1 tablespoon bonemeal
1½ teaspoons dried yeast
2 oz (55g) dried skimmed milk
1 teaspoon garlic granules
1 tablespoon dried parsley
1 teaspoon poppy seeds
1 tablespoon pumpkin seeds
2 teaspoons sunflower seeds
1 oz (30g) organic carrot, grated
¼ apple, finely chopped
1 tablespoon green nori flakes
12 fl oz (340ml) Meaty Brew, Fish Brew or Veggie Brew (pages 73, 88,104) with 1 teaspoon Marmite
1 free-range egg, beaten

Mix the dry ingredients together. Add all the other ingredients and mix thoroughly. Knead and roll out to ¼ or ½ an inch depending on the size of dog. Using a bone-shaped cutter, make the biscuits and place on a floured baking tray. Bake at 300°F for 35–40 minutes. Turn the oven off and let the biscuits dry out in the oven for 5–7 hours.

For a treat, mix a tablespoon of carob powder with 1½ teaspoons water and spread on the biscuits. Put in the refrigerator to harden.

Makes about 36 biscuits – they should be stored in the refrigerator.

This recipe has been concocted as a thank you to all the dogs who have been willing tasters of the recipes in this book. We have tried to combine their favourite ingredients and, judging by how they all devoured these Titbits, we guess we got it right. It would be impossible to list all the dogs who have tried our dog food but we would like to give a special mention to the following:

Wilfred Ashby – Welsh Springer Spaniel
Bear and Mistie Ashcroft – Newfoundlands
Maisie Banfield – Wire-haired Dachshund
Zoe Barc – German Shepherd Dog/Labrador Retriever
Roscoe Bastedo – Dobermann
Charley Baxter – Golden Retriever
Bertie Bentley – Golden Retriever
Luke Berridge – Labrador Retriever
Barty Blythe – Labrador/Collie Cross
Bigsby Boutwood – Labrador Retriever Cross
Ben Buchner – Alsatian
Liffey Butterworth – Labrador Retriever
Troy Butterworth – Collie Cross
Bannock and Oliver Cammack – English Springer Spaniels
Bella Capelin – Border Terrier
Hamish Carswell – Golden Retriever/Collie
Penny Connell – Lurcher
Ollie Daniel – Lurcher
Sam Daniel – Collie
Tippy Daws – Collie/Mix
Bagheera Dembinsky – Labrador Retriever
Brett Denison – Welsh Corgi
Golly Deveries – Welsh Collie
Dudley Edward – English Springer Spaniel/Mix
Scrappy Elliott – Shih-Tzu/Jack Russell/Mix
Bertie Evans – Bernese Mountain Dog
Oscar Evans – Yorkshire Terrier
Scamp Farmer – Wire-haired Fox Terrier

Gary Flind – Pug
Sidney Flind – English Bull Terrier
Daisy and Araminta Gale – Cavalier King Charles Spaniels
Daisy and Little Dorrit Garland – Dobermanns
Champers Goodwin – Lurcher
Kulu Green – Dobermann Pinscher Cross
Wooster Gudgeon – Labrador Retriever
Domino Hammond – Border Collie
Noodles Hardy – English Bull Terrier
Tessa Hedgecock – English Springer Spaniel
Darcey Heyes – English Setter
Holly Horne – English Springer Spaniel
Holly Houseman – Great Dane
Jade Howling – Rottweiler
Meg Leaver – Cavalier King Charles Spaniel
Jody Lillywhite – Labrador Retriever
Gemma Luffingham – Boxer
Andy Martin – Italian Spinone
Sky Martin – English Bulldog
Bobby Mash – Cocker Spaniel
Dazy Mash – Cocker Spaniel
Buster Melling – English Springer Spaniel
Nell Meyer – Golden Retriever
Tor Moores – Labrador Retriever
Jade Morgan – Labrador Retriever
Poppy Oldham – Labrador Retriever
Milly Pine – Bearded Collie Cross
Fey and Tosh Prescott – Lurchers
Flynn Prescott – Greyhound
Waldo Remington – Collie/Jack Russell Cross
Kilda Rhodes – Cairn Terrier
Percy Rowlands – Yorkshire Terrier
Gromit Stickland – Jack Russell Terrier
Poppy and Rebecca Stoddard – Jack Russell Terriers
Satchmo Sweet – Labrador Retriever/English Springer Spaniel Cross
Daisy Timothy – Flat-coated Retriever
Millie Timothy – Golden Retriever
Morgan Timothy – Labrador Retriever
Sally Townsend – Greek Heinz 57

Della Turner – Miniature long-haired Dachshund
Zea Turner – Dobermann
Pippin Woolnough – Lurcher
Holly Wright – English Springer Spaniel
Fred and Snoopy Young – Basset Hounds

DIETS FOR DIFFERENT AGES

'You cannot teach old dogs new tricks.'

Proverb

Puppies, adolescents, adults and senior citizens – in the wild they would all have eaten the same things. However, they would have devoured a whole raw rabbit, pheasant, hare or partridge and these are perfect foods. Animals fed on such a natural diet would experience very few health problems in old age. That isn't the case in our modern world of pollutants and pesticides, and puppies and older dogs therefore need different diets.

Puppies must eat the right things for optimum development and do not fare well on a cheap all-in-one dried food, semi-moist preparation or canned food. Equally, a senior citizen cannot cope with some of the impure foods that an adolescent or adult can tolerate. If a dog is fed meals of minimum nutritional value its health is bound to suffer in later years. It will get heart problems, diabetes, thyroid, pancreatic and intestinal disorders, liver and kidney trouble or even cancer, unless the symptoms are spotted early and the diet changed.

Puppies aged between two and three months should be fed four meals a day. The proportions should be roughly 75 per cent to 25 per cent in the order in which the ingredients appear.

PERFECT PUPPY MENU

Morning
Weetabix and goats' milk

Mid-day
Scrambled eggs and raw tripe

Afternoon
Cooked chicken mince and biscuit meal

Evening
Raw tripe and biscuit meal

If you don't have time to make home-made meals adding good supplements of calcium and phosphorus and bonemeal, Pedigree Chum Puppy Food is recommended by the Akita breeder, Jo Gibbs. We suggest that for biscuit meal you use Beta Puppy Meal. Farley's Rusks and small raw carrots can be given as treats and are particularly good for puppies' teeth.

Puppies aged between three and six months should have three meals a day; i.e. cut out the midday meal. At the age of nine months they have more or less stopped growing and should have one main meal or two smaller meals per day. A dog's digestive system takes about eight hours so you would be advised to feed the main meal in the morning. That way you won't have to get up in the middle of the night!

IDEAL ADULT DOG DIET

According to our research the majority of breeders, kennel owners and vets, advocate raw green tripe and plain biscuit as the main meal (50/50 ratio). Tripe is the part of the animal which is rich in grains and grasses, and in the wild a dog would always eat the stomach and liver of its prey first. There is a supreme irony in writing a book about healthy cooking for dogs and advocating the above recipe, but it would be unethical for us to do otherwise. Raw green tripe and plain biscuit are the healthiest meal. And the best treats are also natural – uncooked shank bones, raw carrots, cabbage, cauliflower and broccoli stalks are far better than crunchy chews that (if you read the small print) contain animal derivatives and sugars. The only exception we would make to this diet would be for an aggressive dog, who would fare better on a cooked chicken and rice or a totally vegetarian diet.

GERIATRIC DOG DIET

If a dog has been fed on raw green tripe all its life it should be unnecessary to change its food and longevity should be assured. However, if you have been taking short-cuts with inexpensive cans, dried foods or semi-moist meals then there is a possibility that there will be problems in later life. Vet Mark Elliott has come up with specific menus for particular diseases. If we had to pick one general recipe for an older dog it would be cooked chicken or rabbit with boiled brown rice and carrots and broccoli. If a dog is fed on 'instant' foods all its life its intestinal tract will be less than robust and a geriatric diet is called for.

If you have to feed an instant meal we recommend Pedigree Puppy cans and Denes in puppyhood, and for adults Naturediet or Butcher's Tripe and Chicken (contains 16 per cent tripe and 16 per cent chicken). Denes tins for the older dog are good, and of the dried foods the more expensive range like Hills, Eukanuba and James Wellbeloved are the best. We do not advocate any semi-moist foods because of the sugar content.

CREAM CAKE SLUSH

'Wilson [Elizabeth Barrett Browning's maid] did not begrudge the little dog his extra cakes and the cream from the milk (for Flush preferred milk to water) . . .'

from *Lady's Maid*
by Margaret Forster

2 oz (55g) banana, mashed
½ teaspoon honey
1 tablespoon natural yoghurt
1 oz (30g) KemKibble (page 108)

Mix all the ingredients together.

STONE SOUP

In Scottish legend there is the story about Stone Soup. A weary traveller disguised as a monk accompanied by his faithful dog arrived at a remote cottage in the Highlands asking the crofter for a bed for the night. He was offered a place in the barn, but what about some sustenance for him and his dog? He ventured to ask for a pot and a wee dram of water saying he would make some soup with a stone he had found on his journey. Having achieved the pot and water into which he dropped his stone, he bravely enquired if there might be an old meat bone, meekly followed by a request for a dried-up turnip. Continuing in this manner he soon had a bubbling brew of meat bone, turnip, carrots, potatoes, leeks and a pinch of salt – not forgetting the vital ingredient, the stone. This can't have been the first time 'the monk' used this method to get his supper because as soon as the crofter turned his back, he whispered to his dog, 'We mustn't forget the thyme', as he dug into his jacket pocket for their favourite seasoning.

I have found that the flavour of this soup is enhanced and goes a wee bit further if you use a stone that has a naturally formed hole in it!

16 oz (455g) meat bones
40 fl oz (2 pints UK/2½ pints USA) cold water
a pinch of salt
a pinch of thyme
1 stone
1 turnip, peeled and chopped
2 carrots, sliced
1 potato, diced
1 leek, sliced

Bring the meat bones, water, salt, thyme and stone to the boil and simmer for an hour. Add the vegetables and simmer for a further 20 minutes. Allow to cool. Remove the meat from the bones. Discard the bones and the stone! Mix in the meat with the rest of the soup. You can either serve the soup as it is, or blend it to soften the meat so that it is more easily digested by an older dog.

ON ALL FOURS

4 oz (115g) tripe
4 oz (115g) liver
4 oz (115g) carrots, sliced
4 oz (115g) brown rice, cooked in boiling water for 30–35 minutes

Wash the tripe and put in boiling water. Simmer for 45 minutes. Add the liver and carrots to the tripe. Simmer for a further 15 minutes. Drain. Allow to cool before chopping the tripe and liver into bite-sized portions. Mix all the ingredients with the brown rice. Made in this proportion, there is enough for a couple of meals.

Older dogs need less fat, easily digested protein and increased amounts of vitamins and mineral, so this would be an ideal meal to feed to your ageing friend.

NANA'S NURSERY NIBBLES

'As they were poor, owing to the amount of milk the children drank, this nurse was a prim Newfoundland dog, called Nana . . . She believed to her last day in old-fashioned remedies like rhubarb leaf, and made sounds of contempt over all this new-fangled talk about germs, and so on.'

from *Peter Pan*
by J. M. Barrie

2–3 slices stoneground wholemeal bread made with sunflower seeds and honey, sliced and cut into cubes
Marmite, Yeast Extract, Vegemite or Vitamite

Place the bread cubes on a baking tray and cook in the oven at 300°F for 25 minutes. Put a little Marmite, Yeast Extract, Vegemite or Vitamite on each piece – your puppy will be begging for more . . .

Nana's advice was good – rhubarb or rhubarb tablets are given to treat constipation. However, a word of warning: don't use rhubarb over a long period as it could prove too acidic for your dog.

SPOT'S SHUTTLE DELIGHT

'Old Mother Shuttle,
Lived in a coal-scuttle
Along with her dog and her cat;
What they ate I can't tell,
But 'tis known very well
That not one of the party was fat.'

from *Mother Shuttle*
Traditional Nursery Rhyme

4 oz (115g) lean beef, minced
2 oz (55g) swede, peeled and diced
2 oz (55g) carrots, sliced
1 free-range egg, hard-boiled and chopped
1 teaspoon bonemeal

Boil the beef and vegetables in a small amount of water for 20 minutes. Drain, retaining the liquid. Add the egg and bonemeal. Moisten with liquid if desired.

This is a good diet for keeping your dog's weight under control.

BUM CHOICE

'He's a little dog, with a stubby tail,
And a moth-eaten coat of tan,
And his legs are short, of the wabbly sort;
I doubt if they ever ran;
And he howls at night, while in broad daylight
He sleeps like a bloomin' log,
And he likes the food of the gutter breed;
He's a most irregular dog.'

from *Bum*
by W. Dayton Wedgefarth

4 oz (115g) liver, chopped
1 teaspoon unrefined corn oil
2 free-range eggs, beaten
1 teaspoon parsley, chopped
1 teaspoon cod-liver oil
2 oz (55g) KemKibble (page 108)

Fry the liver in the corn oil for six to eight minutes. Add the eggs, parsley and cod-liver oil. Cook the mixture slowly, stirring occasionally until the egg has set. Mix in the KemKibble.

This is a good recipe for an older dog and should be served in small portions two or three times a day. An older dog doesn't need as much food as a young active dog, but it's important that an older dog should have a sufficient intake of vitamin D, calcium and phosphorus.

OLD CAVALL'S DIET

King Arthur had a dog called Cavall and it is said that the dog's footprints are immortalised in stone in Wales.

4 oz (115g) chicken, beef, rabbit or venison, cooked and minced
2 oz (55g/⅓ cup) brown rice, cooked in boiling water for 30–35 minutes
1 oz (30g) carrot, grated
1 oz (30g) broccoli florets, cooked
1 free-range egg, hard-boiled and chopped
Canine Care Essential Oils
Canine Care Vitamin/Mineral Supplement

Mix the meat, brown rice, carrot, broccoli florets and egg together. Just before serving, add the Canine Care Essential Oils and Canine Care Essential Vitamin/Mineral Supplement, according to the amounts specified on the packaging.

This diet is recommended for older dogs. If your pet is suffering from arthritis, Canine Care Essential Oils in his food should ease this condition.

RECIPES FOR AILING DOGS

'With dogs you can feed good, indifferent or bad health.'
from *The Complete Herbal Handbook for the Dog and Cat*
by Juliette de Bairacli Levy

Most dogs like garlic crushed and cooked in their food and it should help keep the fleas away as well as strengthening the digestive system. Garlic can eliminate worms and it is also recommended for dogs suffering hip pain from arthritis or dysplasia. It is said to aid in reducing blood sugar in diabetes.

> '"What does SUGAR spell?" Millicent would ask, and Hector would walk round the tea table to the sugar-bowl and lay his nose against it, gazing earnestly and clouding the silver with his moist breath.'
>
> from *Work Suspended, and Other Stories*
> by Evelyn Waugh

If your dog is suffering from diabetes, its diet should contain more protein and less fat than usual. The aim is to reduce stress on the pancreas, so one should avoid foods containing sugar. The pods of green beans contain certain hormonal substances related to insulin so they are an excellent vegetable to start adding to your dog's diet, along with Jerusalem artichokes, alfalfa sprouts and dandelion greens. With this condition it is best to feed your dog raw lean meat and some uncooked vegetables. The mineral chromium is useful for reducing blood sugar.

> 'If you pick up a starving dog and make him prosperous, he will not bite you. This is the principal difference between a dog and a man.'
>
> from *Pudd'nhead Wilson*
> by Mark Twain

DIET FOR DIABETES

3 oz (85g) lean beef, minced
5 oz (140g/1 cup) brown rice, cooked
1 oz (30g) mixed vegetables, chopped and uncooked (e.g. carrot, onion, parsley, alfalfa sprouts)
½ teaspoon brewer's yeast

or

1 free-range egg
5 oz (140g/1 cup) brown rice, cooked
1 oz (30g) mixed vegetables, chopped and cooked (Jerusalem artichokes, green beans, corn)
½ teaspoon dried skimmed milk

Mix all the ingredients and serve warm.

SKIN DEEP

4 oz (115g) raw lean beef, minced
2½ oz (70g/½ cup) brown rice, cooked in boiling water for 30–35 minutes
1 free-range egg, hard-boiled and chopped
1 oz (30g) carrot, grated
1 tablespoon unrefined vegetable oil
a pinch of sea salt

Mix all the ingredients together and serve.

> This is a particularly good recipe for dogs suffering from skin conditions and a lacklustre coat. It is high in protein and moderate in carbohydrates and fats. The skin vitamins and minerals that can be added are vitamin E, sulphur and zinc.

WESSEX WEIGHT WATCHING DIET

'I live here: Wessex is my name;
I am a dog known rather well:
I guard the house; but how that came
To be my whim I cannot tell.'

from *A Popular Personage at Home*
by Thomas Hardy

Thomas Hardy, the English novelist, poet and dramatist, had a wire-haired Fox Terrier called Wessex (Wessie for short) who ruled the house. Wessie was insistent about listening to his favourite radio programmes, slept on the sofa and would jump on the table at mealtimes and attempt to grab the food off visitors' forks!

4 oz (115g) extra-lean beef, rabbit, venison or pigeon, cooked and cut into bite-sized pieces
1 oz (30g) carrot, grated
½ apple, grated
1 oz (30g) spring greens, chopped and cooked
2 oz (55g) cottage cheese
1 oz (30g) fresh egg noodles, cooked in boiling water for three to four minutes (optional)
Canine Care Vitamin/Mineral Supplement
Canine Care Antioxidant

Mix the meat, carrot, apple, spring greens, cottage cheese and egg noodles together. Just before serving, add the Canine Care Essential Vitamin/Mineral Supplements and Canine Care Antioxidant, according to the amounts specified on the packaging.

We recommend this diet for dogs suffering from obesity because it is low in calories and highly nutritious.

HECTOR'S HYPOALLERGENIC DIET

'A Foxhound once served me as a guide,
A good one at hill, and at valley;
    But day after day
    He led me astray,
To follow a milk-woman's tally.'

from *Lament Of A Poor Blind*
by Thomas Hood

4 oz (115g) lamb or rabbit, cooked and minced
2 oz (55g/⅓ cup) brown rice, cooked in boiling water for 30–35 minutes
Canine Care Essential Vitamin/Mineral Supplements
Canine Care Antioxidant

Mix the lamb or rabbit and brown rice together. Just before serving, add the Canine Care Essential Vitamin/Mineral Supplements and the Canine Care Antioxidant, according to the amounts specified on the packaging.

BOUNCE BACK BODGER

'The old dog [Bodger], barking wildly, and frantic with anxiety, for he had sensed disaster although he could not see it, waded chest deep into the churning water, but the force knocked him back again, breathless and choking; and he was forced to retreat.'

from *The Incredible Journey*
by Sheila Burnford

4 oz (115g) lean beef, minced
a pinch of salt
2 oz (55g/⅓ cup) brown rice, cooked in boiling water for 30–35 minutes
1 free-range egg, hard-boiled and chopped
1 teaspoon fresh parsley, chopped
1 teaspoon wheatgerm oil

Boil the beef in a little salted water for 15 minutes. Drain, saving the liquid. Mix together the beef, rice, egg and parsley. If you can't get wheatgerm oil, crumble up a wheatgerm tablet and add to the mixture. Pour the warm liquid over the food to give it a moist, easily digested texture.

If your dog is under stress or suffering from nervous exhaustion, this meal is highly recommended.

Bach's Rescue Remedy is also excellent for a dog in a stressed condition.

CAP CANCER

One of Florence Nightingale's earliest patients was a Collie called Cap who belonged to Smither, a local shepherd. At the age of sixteen, Florence Nightingale was walking over the downs near Embley when she came across Cap suffering from a broken leg. There is no doubt that the pleasure it gave her in saving Cap, led her on to dedicating her life to caring for others.

So far nobody has been able to cap cancer, but we do know that there are certain ways of forestalling it, starting with diet. According to the North London vet, John Carter, who has done a lot of research since his own dog died of cancer, organic vegetables and fruit together with raw liver should be high on the list. Recent research also leads us to selenium as an essential trace element needed to help ward off cancer, ageing and infertility. Since the early 1970s, selenium has been added to farm animals' feed in parts of the world where natural selenium levels are low. This includes some areas of Britain, Canada and the United States.

8 oz (230g) raw liver, chopped
4 oz (115g) raw organic carrot, grated
½ oz (15g) Brazil nuts (richest natural source of selenium), ground

Mix all the ingredients and serve.

Supplement your dog's diet with selenium and vitamins A, C and E. You can also give the herb echinacea, which is said to have anti-cancer properties.

KIDNEY KIEV

4 oz (115g) chicken, minced
½ clove garlic, crushed
1 teaspoon unrefined corn oil
3 oz (85g) brown rice, cooked in boiling water for 30–35 minutes
1 free-range egg, hard-boiled and chopped
1 oz (30g) carrot, grated
½ oz (15g) apple, grated
1 teaspoon brewer's yeast

Gently fry the chicken and garlic in the corn oil. Mix with the other ingredients.

> This is a particularly good diet for a dog suffering from kidney disease. You could add to your dog's food some cod-liver oil for vitamin A as well as a vitamin B supplement.

TAMA TORI-NO-TAKIKOMIGOHAN

A noted Japanese Chin was Tama (Japanese for 'jewel') who was owned by the Far Eastern art collector, Henri Cernuschi. Tama had the honour of being painted by both Édouard Manet and Pierre-Auguste Renoir.

1 tablespoon extra virgin olive oil
2 oz (55g) shiitake mushrooms, chopped
3 oz (85g) carrots, sliced
2 oz (55g) bean sprouts
5 fl oz (140ml) water
1 tablespoon tamari soy sauce
½ teaspoon honey
2 oz (55g) tofu, sliced and cubed
3 oz (85g) chicken breast, skinned and chopped into thin strips
2 oz (55g/⅓ cup) brown rice, cooked in boiling water for 30–35 minutes
1 teaspoon green nori flakes

Fry the shiitake mushrooms, carrots and bean sprouts in the olive oil for six minutes. Mix together the water, soy sauce and honey. Add the tofu, chicken and the liquid mixture to the vegetables. Cook for five minutes. Add the brown rice and green nori flakes. Bring to the boil and cook for three to four minutes, until most of the liquid has been absorbed.

This delicious Japanese dish should bring to life any dog suffering from TATT (Tired All The Time).

CONCLUSION

Until writing *Canine Care and Cuisine* with Jeannie, I was as guilty as the next person of succumbing to cheap offers and buying inexpensive dog food in bulk. However, in researching this book I started to read the small print on the tins and was startled to find that, in the majority of cases, the chicken, lamb, beef etc. advertised was a mere 4 per cent of the content while the rest was often called 'animal derivatives or animal by-products'. This effectively meant I didn't know what I was feeding my dogs.

Fortunately I had always given my dogs essential oils, vitamins and minerals which had kept them in good health with glossy coats, but I realised that nutritionally I could be doing better for them. So what did I do? I started to find a moment in my 'instant' life to begin cooking Jeannie's nutritious recipes. Sometimes if we were away I would stock up on tins of Naturediet, Pascoe's Country Dinner or Butcher's Tripe & Chicken, which all have a high meat content and itemise the contents.

I was therefore delighted when our homoeopathic vet Mark Elliott suggested that we bring out our own Canine Care products. But I suspect it's just as well he's a country vet treating pigs, sheep, cows, horses, goats etc, as I've a funny feeling that when all his dog and cat clients start to take our nutritious supplements and foods their vet bills will be down to a minimum and he won't be seeing very much of them!

ALEXANDRA BASTEDO
Almodington, West Sussex

FOOD AND ITS VITAMIN AND MINERAL CONTENT

If you want your dog to be vegetarian, vegan or macrobiotic, a knowledge of foods and their vitamin and mineral content is essential to create a balanced diet. It is also important to understand what value each vitamin and mineral has for your dog.

FOOD VALUES
(Main Components)

Alfalfa	vitamins C, B, D, E & K, calcium & phosphorus
All Bran	fibre, vitamins A, B, C, D, iron & minerals
Apples	fibre, vitamins C, E, B & potassium
Bananas	fibre, vitamins C, E, B6 & potassium
Beans, green	fibre, carbohydrate, vitamins C, B, potassium & iron
Beans, Lima	fibre, protein, vitamins E, B & minerals
Beef	protein, fat, vitamin B12, niacin, thiamin, riboflavin & iron
Beetroot	fibre, vitamins C, E, B, potassium & iron
Bones	minerals, calcium & phosphorus
Bran	thiamine & fibre
Bread	carbohydrate, fibre, sodium, vitamin B & iron
Broccoli	fibre, protein, vitamins C, A, E, B, calcium & magnesium
Brussels sprouts	fibre, carbohydrate, protein, vitamins C, E, B & iron
Bulghur	carbohydrate, protein, vitamin B & minerals
Cabbage	fibre, vitamins C, E, B & minerals
Carrots	carbohydrate, vitamins A, C, E, B & minerals
Cauliflower	fibre, vitamins C, B & minerals
Celery	fibre, vitamins C, B & potassium
Cheese	protein, fat, calcium, vitamin B12 & zinc
Chicken	protein, fat, vitamins E, B, B12 & minerals
Chicken livers	vitamins A, B, B12, C, E, protein, iron, fat & zinc
Cod	protein, fat, vitamins E, B, B12, potassium & sodium
Cod-liver oil	vitaminx D, A, phosphorus, iodine & sulphur
Corn	carbohydrate, fibre, protein, vitamins C, E & B
Cornmeal	fibre, carbohydrate, vitamins B, E, sodium, iron & fat
Corn oil	fat, vitamin E
Cottage cheese	protein, fat, iron, vitamins B12, B & calcium
Courgette/Zucchini	fibre, vitamins A, C, B & potassium
Cucumber	vitamins C, E, B & potassium
Dates	fibre, carbohydrate, vitamin B, potassium & iron

Eggs	protein, fat, vitamins D, E, B, B12 & iron
Flour, wholemeal	carbohydrate, protein, fibre, vitamin B & iron
Garlic	carbohydrate, potassium & calcium
Honey	carbohydrate, riboflavin, iron & potassium
Kelp	vitamins A, B, C, D, E & K & iodine
Kidneys	protein, vitamins B12, B, A, iron, zinc & fat
Lamb	protein, fat, vitamins B12, B, E & minerals
Lentils	protein, vitamins C, E, B, iron & potassium & phosphorus
Lettuce	fibre, vitamins A, C, E & potassium
Liver	protein, fat, vitamins A, B12, B, C, D, E, iron & zinc
Macaroni	carbohydrate, protein, vitamins E, B & iron
Meat	protein, fat, vitamins & minerals
Milk	carbohydrate, protein, fat, vitamins & minerals
Mushrooms	fibre, vitamins C, E, B, potassium & iron
Nettles	vitamin C & iron
Nuts	fat, protein, vitamins E & Bs
Oats	carbohydrate, protein, vitamin B, magnesium & iron
Oils	fat, essential fatty acids, vitamin E
Onion	vitamin C & minerals
Parsley	vitamins A, C, iron, potassium & calcium, phosphorus & manganese
Pasta	carbohydrate, protein, vitamins E, B & iron
Peas	fibre, carbohydrate, protein, vitamins C, B & potassium
Poppy seeds	carbohydrate, fat, protein, calcium, phosphorus, potassium, sodium & magnesium
Potatoes	carbohydrate, phosphorus, potassium, iron, vitamins C & B6
Pumpkin seeds	fat, protein, carbohydrate, calcium, phosphorus, iron & vitamin A
Rabbit	protein, vitamins B12, B, iron & minerals
Rice, brown	carbohydrate, fibre, vitamin E & minerals
Sesame seeds	fat, carbohydrate, calcium, phosphorus, potassium & iron, vitamins A, B1 & B2
Spinach	fibre, carbohydrate, protein, vitamins A, C, E, B & iron

Sunflower seeds	fat, vitamins E & B
Tahini	fat, carbohydrate, calcium, phosphorus, iron, potassium, vitamins A, B1 & B2
Tofu	protein, fat, vitamins B1 & B2, magnesium, calcium, phosphorus, iron & potassium
Tomato purée	carbohydrate, vitamins A, C, B, sodium, potassium & iron
Tripe	protein & fat
Tuna	protein, fat, iron & sodium
Turkey	protein, fat, vitamins B12, B, E, zinc, iron & potassium
Turnips	fibre, carbohydrate, vitamins A, C, E, B & potassium
Wakame	carbohydrate, calcium, phosphorus, iron, sodium, potassium, iodine, vitamins A & C
Yeast	protein, vitamin B, thiamine, riboflavin, calcium & iron
Yoghurt	protein, fat, vitamin B12, riboflavin & calcium

FOODS WHERE VITAMINS AND MINERALS ARE FOUND

Carbohydrates
Whole grains, sugar, syrup, honey, fruits and vegetables.

Fats
Butter, margarine, vegetable oils, fats in meat, whole milk and milk products, nuts (except peanuts) and seeds.

Proteins
Meats, fish, poultry, free-range eggs, whole milk and milk products, soya bean products and whole grains.

Vitamin A
Liver, free-range eggs, yellow fruits and vegetables, dark green fruits and vegetables, whole milk and milk products.

Vitamin B1
Brewer's yeast, whole grains, blackstrap molasses, organ meats, free-range egg yolks, legumes and nuts (except peanuts).

Vitamin B2 (Riboflavin)
Brewer's yeast, whole grains, blackstrap molasses, organ meats, free-range egg yolks, legumes and nuts (except peanuts).

Vitamin B6 (Pyridoxine)
Meats and organ meats, brewer's yeast, whole grains, blackstrap molasses, wheatgerm, legumes and green leafy vegetables.

Vitamin B12 (Cyanocobalamin)
Organ meats, fish, free-range eggs, cheese, whole milk and milk products.

Biotin
Free-range egg yolks, liver, unpolished rice, brewer's yeast, whole grains, sardines and legumes.

Choline
Free-range egg yolks, organ meats, brewer's yeast, wheat germ, soya beans, fish and legumes.

Folic Acid
Dark green leafy vegetables, organ meats, brewer's yeast, root vegetables, whole grains, oysters, salmon, and whole milk.

Inositol
Whole grains, citrus fruits, brewer's yeast, molasses, meat, whole milk, nuts (except peanuts), and vegetables.

Niacin
Lean meats, poultry, fish, brewer's yeast, rice bran, whole milk and milk products.

Pangamic Acid
Brewer's yeast, rare steaks, brown rice, sunflower, pumpkin and sesame seeds.

Para Amino Benzoic Acid (PABA)
Organ meats, wheat germ, yoghurt, molasses and green leafy vegetables.

Pantothenic Acid
Organ meats, brewer's yeast, egg yolks, legumes, whole grains, wheat germ and salmon.

Vitamin C
Citrus fruits, rose hips, acerola cherries, alfalfa seeds, sprouts, cantaloupe, strawberries, broccoli, tomatoes and green peppers.

Vitamin D
Salmon, sardines, herring, vitamin D-fortified milk and milk products, free-range egg yolks and organ meats.

Vitamin E
Cold-pressed oils, eggs, wheat germ, organ meats, molasses, sweet potatoes and leafy vegetables.

Vitamin K
Green leafy vegetables, free-range egg yolks, safflower oil, blackstrap molasses, cauliflower and soya beans.

Bioflavanoids
Fruits, particularly citrus fruits. Blackcurrants and buckwheat are especially rich in bioflavanoids.

Unsaturated Fatty Acids
Vegetable oils and sunflower seeds.

Calcium
Whole milk and milk products, green leafy vegetables, shellfish and molasses.

Chromium
Honey, grapes, raisins, corn oil, whole grain cereals and brewer's yeast.

Cobalt
Organ meat, poultry, whole milk, green leafy vegetables and fruits.

Copper
Organ meats, seafood, nuts (except peanuts), legumes, molasses and raisins.
Iodine
Seafood and kelp.

Iron
Organ meats and meats, eggs, fish, poultry, blackstrap molasses, green leafy vegetables and dried fruits.

Magnesium
Seafood, whole grains, dark green vegetables, molasses and nuts (except peanuts).

Manganese
Whole grains, green leafy vegetables, legumes, nuts (except peanuts), pineapples and egg yolks.

Molybdenum
Legumes, whole grain cereals, whole milk, kidney, liver and dark green vegetables.

Phosphorus
Fish, meats, poultry, eggs, legumes, whole milk and milk products, nuts (except peanuts) and whole grain cereals.

Potassium
Lean meats, whole grains, vegetables, dried fruits, legumes and sunflower seeds.

Sodium
Seafood, celery, processed foods and whole milk products.

Sulphur
Fish, garlic, onions, eggs, meats, cabbage and Brussels sprouts.

Zinc
Pumpkin and sunflower seeds, seafood, organ meats and meats, mushrooms, brewer's yeast, soya beans, herring, eggs and wheat-germ.

VITAMINS AND MINERALS AND WHAT THEY DO

Acidophilus
Maintains a favourable micro-floral balance in the gastro-intestinal tract and may assist the natural digestive processes. Recommended for dogs on long-term antibiotics and steroid medication.

Alfalfa (Medicago sativa)
Native to Europe, Asia and North Africa. Nutritive herb with a high vitamin and mineral content.

Aloe Vera
Native to Africa, aloe has been traditionally used both externally and internally for first aid and skin conditions and as a protective and healing agent in gastrointestinal conditions. Also possesses laxative, anti-inflammatory and antioxidant properties.

Amino Acids
Building blocks of protein with specific uses. Basic function of most amino acids is to supply essential material for duplication of the genetic code, for cell division and for the formation of muscles and connective tissues. Amino acids are classified as 'essential' or 'non-essential'. Essential amino acids cannot be synthesised by the body and must be obtained from food, these are histidine, isoleucine, leucine, lysine, methionine, phenylalanine, threonine, tryptophan and valine. Non-essential amino acids are synthesised from essential amino acids, such as taurine, carnitine and tyrosine.

Betaine
Found in beetroot. Betaine is an intermediate in the conversion of choline to glycine, and helps to break down fats.

Bilberry (Vaccinium myrtillus)
Native to Europe and North America, bilberry's high anthocyanin content gives it antioxidant properties and is known to increase capillary blood circulation, with overall benefits for the eyes and cardiovascular system.

Bioflavanoids
Also known as flavanoids, bioflavanoids are colourful antioxidants found in plants. They aid absorption of vitamin C and maintain the integrity of blood vessels and normal circulation. Some of the common bioflavanoids include: anthocyanidins, hesperidin, myricetin, nobiletin, proanthocyanidins, quercetin and rutin.

Biotin
Involved in energy release form food, carbohydrate and protein metabolism. Required for normal growth and development of bone marrow, fur, skin and muscle.

Boron
Research suggests it may play a role in maintaining healthy, strong bones. Also needed for absorption of calcium.

Boswellia
Antioxidant with anti-inflammatory properties, of particular use in maintaining supple and healthy joints.

Buchu (Barosma betulina)
A traditional South African herb, known for its stimulant, urinary antiseptic, diuretic and carminative action.

Calcium
Works in the body with magnesium and vitamin D and maintains healthy bones and teeth. Helps in the function of nerves and muscles and has a role in the utilisation of amino acids.

Cat's Claw (Uncaris tomentosa)
Traditionally used by the Indians as a powerful immune system booster, anti-inflammatory, muscle-relaxant and for its beneficial cardiovascular effects.

Celery (Apium fruescens)
Native to European countries, celery is a good cleansing and diuretic herb.

Cellulase
An enzyme that breaks down cellulose, used to aid digestion of vegetable matter and fibrous foods.

Chelate
Most minerals are bonded to a chelate (eg. amino acids, aspartates, picolinates and citrates) by a process called chelation; in this form, the mineral achieves maximum absorption.

Chlorella
Green micro-algae, rich in chlorophyll, suggested for the immune system, and detoxifies the liver, blood and bowel from chemicals and heavy metals.

Chondroitin
A glucosaminoglycan that plays an essential role in the formation of joint cartilage.

Chromium
Essential mineral involved in regulating blood sugar levels and carbohydrate, fat, protein and cholesterol metabolism.

Cod-Liver Oil
Source of omega-3 EFAs (EPA and DHA) as well as vitamins A and D, which maintain normal growth, supple joints and healthy fur and skin.

Co-enzyme Q 10
Essential mineral for energy production in all cells, notably those of the heart, muscle tissue, brain and liver. Powerful antioxidant

and important for the immune system and healthy gums.

Collagen

A crude form of 'collagen soup' had been used in the twelfth century to support joint function and maintain joint integrity. It is a low molecular weight protein, consisting of a series of amino acids, and is a building block of bone cartilage, and is responsible for the framework and shape of connective tissue.

Colloidal Minerals

Microscopic particles, which in the presence of amino acids, form chelated minerals and organic colloids ('crystalloids'). In this form they are readily absorbed by the intestinal mucosa.

Copper

Required for red blood cell formation and involved in several enzyme systems. Helps utilise iron, and aids development of bone, brain and nerve tissue.

Cranberry

Known to restore a healthy acid balance in the urinary tract, also has antibacterial properties.

Cysteine

An amino acid that contributes to the structure of proteins and plays an important role in energy metabolism.

Dandelion (Taraxacum officinale)

Dandelion grows wild in most parts of the world and is known for its powerful and safe diuretic properties. It is an effective detoxifying herb.

Devil's Claw (Harpagophytum rocumbens)

This African plant derives its name from the appearance of its tough, barbed fruit. It is used traditionally for inflammation and swelling in arthritic conditions.

Echinacea (Echinacea spp)

Native to North America, known to possess anti-bacterial and anti-viral properties, and is useful in strengthening the immune system.

Evening Primrose Oil

Rich source of gamma-linolenic acid (GLA) and linoleic acid (LA), which are polyunsaturated essential fatty acids (EFAs). These are for cell membrane growth and for the production of prostaglandins which are involved in regulating the nervous, cardiovascular and reproductive systems, skin conditions and other biological functions.

Feverfew (Tanacetum parthenium)

Originally from south-eastern Europe, feverfew is known to possess analgesic properties. Has anti-inflammatory properties and reduces body temperature.

Folic Acid

Important in the formation of red blood cells. Also for a healthy nervous system and RNA/DNA development. Also has a role in protein metabolism and prevents anaemia.

Garlic (Allium sativum)

Originally from central Asia, garlic is now grown worldwide. Benefits the digestive and immune systems and assists in maintaining a healthy heart, circulation and normal cholesterol levels. Also known to display anti-bacterial anti-fungal and anti-viral properties.

Glucosamine

Building blocks of the proteoglycans, the basic substance of cartilage. For healthy joint care.

Iodine

Utilised by the thyroid gland to produce hormones which help regulate the metabolism.

Iron

Required in formation of haemoglobin. Oxygen carrier throughout the body and important for muscle function. Prevents anaemia.

Juniper Berry (Juniperus spp.)
Juniper has been traditionally used in Europe, Asia and North America for its antiseptic properties, commonly for urinary tract infections.

Lecithin
An emulsifier of fats, lecithin is a source of many nutrients, notably phosphatidyl choline which is involved in biological functions in cell membranes, cardiovascular and nervous systems and the mechanisms that store and transport fats and cholesterol.

Leucine
An amino acid involved in stress, energy and muscle metabolism.

Liquorice Root (Glycyrrhiza glabra)
Native to south-eastern Europe and south-western Asia, known traditionally for its powerful anti-inflammatory, demulcent and expectorant properties. It is broken down to glycyrrhizin in the gut which has an anti-inflammatory effect, particularly useful for inflammatory conditions of the digestive system and joints.

Lysine
An amino acid involved in energy production, regulating calcium absorption, collagen production, neurotransmitter and other amino acid production.

Magnesium
Constituent of skeletal structure and teeth. Role as a co-factor for energy production. Vital for nerve transmission, muscles and a proper heart beat. Required for absorption of calcium and potassium.

Manganese
Co-factor for many body enzymes. Responsible for various functions such as synthesis of bone/cartilage, superoxide dismutase (SOD helps prevent tissue damage due to free radicals), protein synthesis and energy production.

Meadowsweet (Filipendula ulmaria)
Native to Europe, meadowsweet contains salicylates and tannins which gives it anti-inflammatory, astringent and diuretic properties.

Methionine
An amino acid involved in the production of other sulphur amino acids.

Omega 3 EFAs
Converted in the body to Eicosapentaenoic acid (EPA) and Docosahexaenoic acid (DHA) and prostoglandins. EPA is believed to have an anti-inflammatory role with healing properties, to maintain healthy joints and cardiovascular system. DHA is thought to play an important part in the transmission of electrical impulses to the brain.

Phosphorus
Important role in skeletal structure. Required for nerve and muscle function.

Potassium
Important for nerve transmission, maintaining normal heart rate and as an electrolyte to maintain correct fluid balance and healthy muscle function.

Propolis
Known to possess antioxidant and anti-bacterial activities and is an immune system enhancer.

Protease
Protein digesting enzyme.

Pumpkin Seed (Cucurbita pepo)
A popular medicinal plant in the Americas, the seeds are rich in EFAs which have anti-inflammatory effects.

Rose Hips
Natural source of vitamin C and bioflavanoids.

Rutin
Bioflavanoid found in buckwheat.

Silica
Rich in glycosaminoglycans which are components of bone, cartilage and arterial tissue. They are also involved in maintaining normal regulation of the heart, brain and peripheral circulation.

Skullcap (Scutellaria lateriflora)
A native North American herb, it is known as a nerve tonic, and helps to support and nourish the nervous system and calms and relieves stress and anxiety.

Spirulina
One of nature's original wholefoods, it grows as a dark plankton in the oceans of the world, serving as a basic link in the food chain. One of the richest sources of highly digestible proteins, this algae also contains vitamins, minerals, enzymes and other nutrients e.g. linoleic acids, vitamin B12, vitamin E, amino acids, iron, RNA, DNA and chlorophyll. Also aids the immune system.

Starflower/Borage Oil
Mixture of mainly mono- and poly-unsaturated oils, one of which is a rich source of GLA, and has approximately 50 per cent more than an equivalent dose of evening primrose oil.

St Johns Wort (Hypericum perforatum)
Native to Europe, herbalists have long used it as a tonic for anxiety. It also has anti-viral, anti-spasmodic and astringent properties.

Taurine
A sulphur amino acid that is the most abundant amino acid in the heart and the second most in the brain. It has neurotransmitter functions and regulates sodium, calcium and potassium levels in cell membranes. It also has antioxidant activity.

Uva Ursi (Arcostaphylos uva-ursi)
Native to Europe, known as one of the best natural urinary antiseptics and diuretics, and may be beneficial in urinary tract infections.

Valerian (Valeriana officinalis)
Native to Europe and northern Asia, valerian has been used in conditions of anxiety, nervous irritability at least since Roman times. Has muscle relaxant properties.

Vitamin A
Important for healthy eyes, skin, hair, bones, teeth and mucous membranes of the respiratory, digestive and urinary tracts.

Vitamin B1
Important for the release of energy from food, maintaining the integrity of the nervous system and several other metabolic functions. It is also needed for normal appetite and growth.

Vitamin B2 (Riboflavin)
Involved in energy release from food. Helps maintain healthy skin, hair, eyes and lining of the nose and throat. Role also in formation of liver enzymes and normal functioning of mental and muscular systems.

Vitamin B3 (Niacin or nicotinic acid)
Energy release from food. Essential for proper function of mental, nervous and digestive systems. Role in formation of red blood cells and steroids, and is needed for healthy circulation.

Vitamin B5 (Pantothenic acid)
Energy release from food. Essential for function of brain, immune system and healthy skin. Considered by many as an 'anti-stress' vitamin. Required for antibody formation, wound healing and growth.

Vitamin B6 (Pyridoxine)
Energy release from food. Important for fat and amino acid metabolism. Required for production of red blood cells and maintenance of fluid balance and healthy nervous system and brain function.

Vitamin B12 (Cyanocobalamin)
Bone marrow and red blood cell regeneration. DNA synthesis and healthy nervous system.

Vitamin B Complex
Group of 'B' vitamins necessary for proper function of the nervous system and healthy maintenance of skin, hair, eyes, intestinal muscles and liver.

Vitamin C
Necessary for maintenance of collagen, bones, gums, teeth and blood capillaries. Aids iron absorption and utilisation of folic acid. Antioxidant properties – protects against damage to vitamins A and E. Involved in cell/tissue repair. Role in formation of red blood cells and adrenal gland hormones. Helps to maintain the immune system and normal cholesterol levels.

Vitamin D
Required for absorption of calcium and phosphorus to maintain healthy bones, teeth, skin, heart, nerves and thyroid.

Vitamin E
Powerful antioxidant, prevents oxidation of certain fats and vitamins. Helps to maintain normal blood clotting and red blood cell integrity. Plays an important role in maintaining healthy function of the cardiovascular and reproductive systems and healthy skin condition.

Vitamin K
Essential for blood clotting and plays a role in the maintenance of healthy bones.

Zinc
Key role in maintenance of nervous, reproductive and immune systems. Required for sensation of taste and smell. Integral part of insulin and required for blood sugar levels. Role in certain enzyme catalysis. Helps wound healing, normal growth, good vision and maintenance of healthy skin.

OKAY OILS

The best oils for cooking are unrefined, cold-pressed oils. Although they may be more expensive than other oils, you will find you don't have to use as much. The cold-pressed form of olive oil is called 'extra-virgin' – if it refers to 'pure' that means petro-chemical extraction. Avoid solvent-expressed oils – by the time the chemical solvent, caustic soda and bleaching processes have done their worst, there is not much goodness left. If you can get hold of them, coconut oil and palm oil are excellent for cooking at high temperatures, followed by extra virgin olive oil for moderate heat, and sesame seed oil and flax-seed oil for low-heat cooking. Corn oil, grapeseed oil, groundnut oil, safflower oil and sunflower oil can also be used in any of the recipes in this book. When using oil for stir-frying, add a little water to the oil, as this stops the oil molecules from overheating. Otherwise check the proportion of saturates, mono-unsaturates and poly-unsaturates: oils with a high saturate and mono-unsaturate content are better for heating than those with a high poly-unsaturate content. Always store oils in a cool, dark place.

CONVERSION TABLES

Liquid Measurements

Imperial	Recommended ml
1 fl oz	30 ml
2 fl oz	55 ml
3 fl oz	85 ml
4 fl oz (¼ pint USA)	115 ml
5 fl oz (¼ pint UK)	140 ml
6 fl oz	170 ml
7 fl oz	200 ml
8 fl oz (½ pint USA)	230 ml
9 fl oz	255 ml
10 fl oz (½ pint UK)	285 ml
11 fl oz	315 ml
12 fl oz	340 ml
13 fl oz	370 ml
14 fl oz	400 ml
15 fl oz	430 ml
16 fl oz (1 pint USA)	455 ml
17 fl oz	485 ml
18 fl oz	515 ml
19 fl oz	540 ml
20 fl oz (1 pint UK) fl oz	570 ml

Solid Measurements

Imperial	Recommended g
1 oz	30 g
2 oz	55 g
3 oz	85 g
4 oz (¼ pound)	115 g
5 oz	140 g
6 oz	170 g
7 oz	200 g
8 oz (½ pound)	230 g
9 oz	255 g
10 oz	285 g
11 oz	315 g
12 oz (¾ pound)	340 g
13 oz	370 g
14 oz	400 g
15 oz	430 g
16 oz (1 pound)	455 g

1 kilogram (kg) equals 2.2 lbs

Useful Equivalents

1.76 UK pints	= 1 litre
2 USA pints	= 1 quart
4 USA quarts	= 1 gallon
1 UK cup	= 10 fl oz
1 USA cup	= 8 fl oz

N.B. The cups referred to in the recipes are USA cups.

Measuring Spoons

(approximate universal conversion)

¼ teaspoon	= 1.25 ml
½ teaspoon	= 2.5 ml
1 teaspoon	= 5 ml
1 tablespoon	= 15 ml

Useful Measurements

3 mm	⅛ inch
6 mm	¼ inch
1 cm	½ inch
2 cm	¾ inch
2.5 cm	1 inch
5 cm	2 inches

Oven Temperatures

C	F	Gas Mark
70	150	
80	175	
100	200	
110	225	¼
120	250	½
140	275	1
150	300	2
160	325	3
180	350	4
190	375	5
200	400	6
220	425	7
230	450	8
240	475	9
260	500	
270	525	
290	550	

MY PREFERRED PRODUCTS

DOG BEDS

There are all manner of beds that my dogs like. However, for all the expensive beds available a dog can be just as happy with a sturdy wooden box with Vet bed in the bottom or an old towel. Dogs also have a mind of their own and will find their own comfortable places if you let them. For the pampered pet Treasurecots Pet Beds are the most luxurious dogs' beds. I first found them at Harrods (at vast expense) but you can order direct (see Product Suppliers). However they are not suitable for chewers or diggers.

DOG BOWLS

For the summer I prefer large bottles which fit upside down into a large dish so there can be no chance of the dog drinking all the water. However, if they have access to the great outdoors they are just as likely to drink from a puddle of non-chlorinated water. Non-spill bowls are ideal for travelling in cars (see Comfy Pet and People Products at Product Suppliers at rear of book). For food I prefer heavyweight bowls which are easily cleaned and cannot get broken. There are also some excellent canine picnic hampers which are very good for travelling and are available from the Bones Catalogue (see Product Suppliers). For a small dog a timer bowl with a forty-eight-hour clock can be a valuable asset if you keep irregular hours as you can set it to open while you are out.

DOG FLAPS

Little Dorrit has one that she pushes outwards with her nose so it slides along her back. Roscoe couldn't cope with that and has his own in another door which has two small plastic doors that open outwards.

DOG FLEA PRODUCTS

An excellent anti-parasite shampoo with an anti-parasite tonic is Corpore Sano (available mail-order from the Sloane Square Health Shop in London). However, if you shampoo your dog be careful to do so on a hot day or dry it thoroughly so it doesn't get chilled.

DOG FOOD

I alternate commercially prepared foods like Naturediet and Butcher's Tripe and chicken with cooking nutritional food for my dogs.

All-in-one Biscuit Meals

There are many on the market but the only ones I will buy as they have either less or no additives, chemicals, preservatives, colourants or sugars are: James Wellbeloved, Burns, Nutro, Hills, Eukanuba IAMS or Techni-Cal.

FLEA COLLARS FOR DOGS

Fleas can cause such problems with skin disorders and worms that reluctantly I will use chemicals to keep them at bay.

Herbal flea collars containing citronella, lemon grass, eucalyptus and lavender are non-chemical and excellent. However, the collars have to be kept topped up with the herbal remedies for maximum efficacy. Also check the dog's neck regularly for an allergic reaction.

FLEXIS

Retractable leads. A wonderful device as a dog can still get a reasonable amount of exercise, particularly in areas that say 'keep your dog on a lead'.

HALTIS

Produced by Dr Roger Mugford, a brilliant invention. Like a horse's head collar it gives you control of the face (not the neck which is much stronger) and the piece round the muzzle tightens if the dog pulls excessively. This also gives good control over an aggressive dog.

LOUNGERS

The Franley PVC Pet Lounger is perfect for arthritic and incontinent dogs.

MUZZLES

Also by Dr Roger Mugford. What dogs did before he came along I don't know. Muzzles used to be hard and scratchy. Dr Mugford's are soft plastic and much kinder to the wearer. Cloth muzzles are not so good in summer, since they are too confining as a dog needs to sweat through its tongue.

SHAMPOOS

Johnson's Baby Shampoo, Corpore Sano anti-parasite shampoo and coal tar and sulphur shampoos.

SUPPLEMENTS

Canine Care Range

Canine Care Essential Vitamins, Canine Care Essential Oils, Canine Care Multi-Mineral and Canine Care Antioxidant.

Denes

Greenleaf, garlic and seaweed.

Bob Martin

Tender Loving Care – vitamin supplement for elderly pets.

Phillips Stress

Calcium and phosphorus with vitamins A and D.

Animal Actives

Animal Magic Royale – a liquid with Royal jelly, ginseng, damiana and capsicum.

Kali – a mixture of Western and Chinese herbs, good for many chronic diseases including arthritis and eczema.

TONICS

Corpore Sano anti-parasite tonic.

WORMERS

Endorid, Panacur and Drontal are obtainable from vets.

PRODUCT SUPPLIERS

The following are products which have been recommended by dog experts and breeders:

Acorn Supplements Ltd
P O Box 103
Robertsbridge
East Sussex TN32 5ZT
Tel: 01580 881333

(Homoeopathic worming and Excel Coat plus.)

Ainsworth Homoeopathic Pharmacy
36 New Cavendish Street
London W1M 7LH
Tel: 0171 935 5330
Fax: 0171 486 4313

Animal Actives
11 Southgate Road
Potters Bar
Hertfordshire EN6 5DR
Tel: 01707 646948
Fax: 01707 646948

(Natural pet products for positive pet health – slippery elm complex, canidor, euphrasia, echinacea.)

Animal Fair
17 Abingdon Road
Kensington
London W8 6AH
Tel: 0171 937 0011

(One of the best pet shops in London; major stockists of most products.)

Animals First
Unit 3, The Royston Centre
Lynchford Road
Ash Vale, Aldershot
Hampshire GU12 5PQ
Tel: 01252 372255
Fax: 01252 372233

(Techni-Cal Pet Food – soya free. Supported by the Canadian Veterinarian and Medical Association for its nutritional quality.)

Arden Grange International Limited
London Road
Albourne
Hassocks
East Sussex BN6 9BJ
Tel: 01273 833390
Fax: 01273 833612

(The complete dry pet food, fresh chicken is the number one ingredient – mail order.)

Edward Baker Ltd
Windham Road
Sudbury
Suffolk CO10 6XD

(Baker's Complete Light [low-fat food] for dogs with a tendency to put on weight. Elite & Omega – dry dog food.)

Biggles
66 Marylebone Lane
London W1M 5FF
Tel: 0171 224 5937
Fax: 0171 935 8454

(Finest special recipe sausages – 85 per cent meat, including lamb and mint, lamb and rosemary, chicken and tarragon sausages. Pork is not the best meat for dogs.)

The Bob Martin Company
Wemberham Lane
Yatton
North Somerset BS19 4BS
Tel: 01934 838061
Fax: 01934 876184

(Private family firm founded in 1892 – many excellent products including natural flea repellent collars and wormers. Main outlets: Tesco, Sainsbury, Safeway, Asda and most pet stores.)

Bones Dog & Catalogue
The Upper Mill
Coln St Aldwyns
Cirencester
Gloucestershire GL7 5AJ
Tel: 01285 750 007
Fax: 01285 750 100

(Their catalogue includes flea patrol bandannas, flea patrol bandanna oil, non-spill water bowl, the mudlark [car seat cover], pets' picnic box, etc.)

J.L. Bragg Ltd
30 Greyfriars Road
Ipswich
Suffolk IP1 1UP
Tel: 01473 252714
Fax: 01473 288947

(Medicinal charcoal biscuits and tablets.)

Burns Pet Nutrition (John Burns BVMS Lic.Ac. MRCVS)
4 Avalon Court
Kidwelly
Carmarthenshire SA17 5EJ
Tel: 01554 890482

(Real food for dogs recommended for eczema, itchy skin, ears, digestive problems, arthritis, rheumatism, heart disease, bad breath, excess moulting, unpleasant body odours and obesity.)

Butcher's Pet Care Ltd
Baker Group House
Crick
Northamptonshire NN6 7TZ
Tel: 01788 823711
Fax: 01788 825247
Sales Fax: 01788 824087

Chlorella Products Ltd
The Stables, Upper Farm
Hinton Parva, Swindon
Wiltshire SN4 0DH
Tel: 01793 791111
Fax: 01793 791122

(Chlorella, Chlorella Growth Factor, KDF/GAC Water Filter.)

Comfy Pet & People Products
2–4 Parsonage Street
Bradninch, Nr. Exeter
Devon EX5 4NW
Tel: 01392 881285
Fax: 01392 881188

(Their brochure includes Waggers products, dog dri-bags, car seat protectors, plastic ventilated beds, dog food/water bowl holders, non-spill water bowls for cars and herbal flea collars.)

Denes Natural Pet Care Limited
2 Osmond Road
Hove
East Sussex BN3 1TE
Tel: 01273 325364
Fax: 01273 325704

(Denes range of complete foods and herbal medicines – ring for nearest stockist or mail order.)

Dogwoode First Aid Kit for Dogs
907 Nell Gwynn House
Sloane Avenue
London SW3 3HB
Tel: 0171 584 6474
Fax: 0171 589 7503

Forbes Copper
Garston House
Sixpenny Handley
Salisbury
Wiltshire SP5 5PB
Tel: 01725 552300
Fax: 01725 552558

(Copper dog collars for rheumatism and arthritis.)

Freshlands
196 Old Street
London EC1V 9FR
Tel: 0171 490 3170
Fax: 0171 490 3170

(Organic foods and natural remedies.)

Fur, Feather & Fins
54 Elm Grove
Southsea
Hampshire PO5 1JG
Tel: 01705 862935
Fax: 01705 817742

(Stockists of multiple pet products.)

G.S.D. Pet Foods
16 Lawrence Crescent
Dinham Road, Caerwent
Newport
Gwent NP6 4NS
Tel: 01291 421004

(100 per cent natural dog food.)

Green Ark Animal Nutrition
Unit 7B, Lineholme Mill
Burney Road
Todmorden
West Yorkshire OL14 7DH
Tel: 01706 812188
Fax: 01706 812188

(Herbal tonic, garlic powder, and many other products, including a Puppy Starter Pack and a Trial Dog Pack.)

Happidog Pet Foods Ltd.
Bridgend, Brownhill Lane
Longton, Preston
Lancashire PR4 4SJ
Tel: 01772 614952
Fax: 01772 614408

(The Original Vegetarian Dog Food full of vitamins and minerals.)

Harrods Ltd
Pet Shop
Brompton Road
Knightsbridge
London SW1X 7XL
Tel: 0171 730 1234
Fax: 0171 581 0470

(Flea patrol bandannas, haltis and Denes pet food.)

Helios Homoeopathics Ltd
89–95 Camden Road
Tunbridge Wells
Kent TN1 2QR
Tel: 01892 515111/511555
Fax: 01892 515116

(The Veterinary Homoeopathy Basic Kit plus individual range.)

Hill's Pet Nutrition Ltd
1 The Beacons
Beaconsfield Road
Hatfield
Hertfordshire AL10 8EQ
Tel: 0800 282 438

(Hill's Prescription Science Diet and Hill's Science Plan – beef from Holland.)

IAMS UK
Unit 2
Meadow Brook Industrial Estate
Maxwell Way
Crawley
West Sussex RH10 2SA
Tel: 01293 572100
Fax: 01293 572130

(Eukanuba dog food contains no artificial colourings, flavouring or preservatives.)

Infinity Foods Co-operative Limited
67 Norway Street
Portslade
East Sussex BN41 1AE
Tel: 01273 424060
Fax: 01273 417739

(Natural and organic foods – retail outlet and wholesale suppliers.)

Johnson's Veterinary Products Ltd.
5 Reddicap Trading Estate
Sutton Coldfield
West Midlands B75 7DF
Tel: 0121 378 1684
Fax: 0121 311 1758

(List of products includes Coal Tar and Sulphur Shampoo and Tea Tree Shampoo, citrus flea repellent and herbal flea collar.)

Mark and Chappell Ltd.
Suite 7G, Britannia House
Leagrave Road
Luton
Bedfordshire LU3 1RJ
Tel: 01582 405006

(Seren-um: for hyperactive and/or aggressive dogs.)

Masters
14 Tews End Lane
Paulerspury
Towcester
Northamptonshire NN12 7NQ
Tel: 01327 811758
Fax: 01327 811699

(Complete Dog Foods – Eclipse and Puppy Food. Contains meat and poultry and no by-products. Linseed is added for glossy coats.)

The Natural Dog Food Co. Ltd.
Audley Street Works
Audley Street
Mossley
Lancashire OL5 9HS
Tel: 01457 835389

(Natural wholefood diet for dogs – vegetarian contains oats, barley, maize, rye, millet, sesame seeds and selected herbs.)

Natural Friends
P O Box 103
Robertsbridge
East Sussex TN32 5ZT
Tel: 01580 881222
Fax: 01580 881444

(Suppliers of flora herbal products, Bach's Flower Remedies, aromatherapy oils, homoeopathic Nelson's products, homoeopathic books, pet memorials, Acorn anal clear, herbal de-wormers, flea collars and flea-clear herbal capsules)

Naturediet Pet Foods Ltd
Pickhurst Road
Chiddingfold
Surrey GU8 4YD
Tel: 01428 682278
Fax: 01428 684968

(Naturediet – home delivery service – excellent moist food with top quality natural ingredients with vitamins and minerals. No added salt and it is free of artificial ingredients, colouring agents, flavour enhancers and processed meats.)

Nelson Homoeopathic Pharmacy
73 Duke Street
London W1M 5DH
Tel: 0171 629 3113
Tel: 0171 495 2404 (mail order)
Fax: 0171 495 0013

Oscar Pet Foods
Pet, Equine & Pigeon Supplies Ltd
Bannister Hall Mill
Higher Walton, Preston
Lancashire PR5 4DB
Tel: 01772 628822
Fax: 01772 628528

(Oscar Original, Premium and Super Premium Complete Dry Dog Food – free home delivery.)

Pascoe's Ltd
Dunball Wharf, Dunball
Bridgwater
Somerset TA6 4TA
Tel: 01278 425939
Fax: 01278 453503

(Their complete food is free from artificial colours, flavours and preservatives and contains vitamins, minerals and oils for a shiny coat.)

Pedigree Petfoods
Melton Mowbray
Leicestershire LE13 0BR
Tel: 01664 410000
Fax: 01664 415232

(Pedigree Veterinary Plan, Pedigree Chum Advance Formula and Pedigree Chum Puppy Food.)

Pets Corner
Country Garden Centre
Bognor Road
Merston
Nr Chichester
West Sussex PO20 6EG
Tel: 01243 530606

(Stockists of multiple dog products – ring 0990 329818 for addresses of other branches in the South.)

Pet Food Warehouse
Quarry Lane Industrial Estate
Chichester
West Sussex PO19 2PS
Tel: 01243 782454
Fax: 01243 531992

(Roger Mugford haltis and muzzles, Seren-um, herbal flea collars, anti-parasite shampoos.)

Pet Nutrition Concepts Ltd
PO Box 201
Chichester
West Sussex PO20 7YT
Tel: 07071 223266

(Suppliers of the Canine Care Range – Essential Vitamins/Multi-Mineral, Antioxidant and Essential Oils.)

PETsMART
Tel: 0990 114499

(Ring for your nearest store – stockists of multiple dog products.)

Pet Pavilion
Chelsea Farmers Market
125 Sydney Street
London SW3 6NR
Tel: 0171 376 8800

(Grooming, food, supplies, accessories and gifts.)

Premium Pet Foods Ltd
Unit 3, Wyvern Way
Uxbridge
Middlesex UB8 2XN
Tel: 01895 810400
Fax: 01895 812397

(Nutro's Natural Choice/Nutro Max – lamb and rice preserved with vitamin E and linoleic acid in the form of sunflower oil – mail order.)

Pure Multi-Nutrients
8 Victory Place
Crystal Palace
London SE19 3RW
Tel: 0181 771 4522
Fax: 0181 771 4522

(Organic foods, natural remedies and macrobiotic foods – mail order.)

Revital Health Shop
35 High Road
London NW10
Tel: 0181 459 3382
Fax: 0181 459 3722
Free phone: 0800 252875

(Mail order – a major stockist of various homoeopathic products and Canine Care products.)

SPR
Poultry and Smallholder Centre
Greenfields Farm, Fontwell Avenue
Eastergate
West Sussex, PO20 6RU
Tel: 01243 542815
Fax: 01243 544662

(Canine Care Range and animal foods.)

Shipton Mill
Long Newnton
Tetbury
Gloucestershire GL8 8RP
Tel: 01666 505050
Fax: 01666 504666

(Various range of organic flours, oats etc. – mail order.)

Sloane Health Shop
32 Sloane Square
London SW1W 8AQ
Tel: 0171 730 7046
Fax: 0171 823 5521

(Mail order throughout th world – various homoeopathic and biochemical remedies, Corpore Sano anti-parasite shampoo and lotion.)

Specialist Pet Foods
P O Box 40
Frimley Green
Camberley
Surrey GU16 6YP
Tel: 01252 834794
Fax: 01252 834592

(Suppliers of Nutrience complete dog foods.)

Spillers Petfood
P O Box 53
Newmarket
Suffolk CB8 8QF
Free phone: 0800 738 2272
Fax: 01638 552299

(Beta, Suprium, Winalot dog food and Bonios.)

Stock Nutrition
Station Road
Yaxham
Norfolk NR19 1RD
Tel: 01362 694957
Fax: 01362 699067

(Genie – bio-degradable disinfectant, Protest – for digestive problems, Moor Gold – holistic tonic for older and nervous dogs and puppies, Dyna-Mite – herbal insect repellent for fleas and Dyna-Mite Shampoo. These products are also available through SPR (David Bland), Greenfields Farm, Fontwell Avenue, Eastergate, West Sussex. Tel: 01243 542815 Fax: 01243 544662.)

Superdogs
1 Green View Cottages
Crambe
York YO6 7JP
Tel: 01653 618736

Plastic Bags (Pooper Scoopers)
(100 bio-degradable bags = £2.50 + 78p P&P, together with A4 sae.)

Thermal Concepts Ltd.
Parc Teifi Business Park
Cardiganshire SA43 1EW
Tel: 01239 614005
Fax: 01239 615191

(Snuffle Safe – microwave heatpad.)

Town and Country Petfoods Ltd
26 Asfordley Road
Melton Mowbray
Leicestershire LE13 0HR
Tel: 01664 63209

(Hi Life Special Care Dog Food with high meat content.)

Treasurecots Pet Beds
Salters Lane
Lower Moor
Worcestershire WR10 2PE
Tel: 01386 860144
Fax: 01386 861427

(Hygienic, non-allergic, draughtproof comfortable dog beds, but not for destructive dogs who shred them when a Comfy Pet ventilated plastic bed would be better.)

Wafcol
Haigh Avenue
South Reddish, Stockport
Cheshire SK4 1NU
Tel: 0161 480 2781
Fax: 0161 474 1896

(Specialist foods for dogs of different ages with different requirements. Also vegetarian and hypo-allergenic. Bonemeal.)

The Watermill
Little Salkeld, Penrith
Cumbria CA10 1NN
Tel: 01768 881523

(Organic dog meal and organic stoneground flours and other organic produce – family-run business with the philosophy 'care for the planet, for sustainable energy and agriculture, for the health of the soil, plants and animals . . .' – mail order catalogue available.)

Weald and Downland Open Air Museum
Singleton, Nr Chichester
West Sussex PO18 0EU
Tel: 01243 811363
Fax: 01243 811475

(Singleton stoneground wholemeal flour.)

James Wellbeloved & Co Ltd
Halfway House
Tintinhull
Nr Yeovil
Somerset BA22 8PA
Tel: 01935 825599
Fax: 01935 823280

(Quality hypo-allergenic complete dog food.)

Wellington Vet Pharmacy
39 Knightsbridge
London SW1X 7NL
Tel: 0171 235 5621
Fax: 0171 235 0158

(The only veterinary pharmacy inside the M25. They stock Nelson's & Weleda homoeopathic products – mail order throughout the world.)

APPROPRIATE ADDRESSES

Agricultural and Veterinary Group of The Royal Pharmaceutical Society of Great Britain (RPSGB)
1 Lambeth High Street
London SE1 7JN
Tel: 0171 735 9141
Fax: 0171 735 7629

Animal Aid
The Old Chapel
Bradford Street
Tonbridge
Kent TN9 1AW
Tel: 01732 364546
Fax: 01732 366533

(Against all animal abuse)

Animal Aunts
45 Fairview Road
Headley Down
Hampshire GU35 8HQ
Tel: 01428 712 611
Fax: 01428 717 190

(A nationwide service providing house and animal sitters)

Animal Health Trust
P O Box 5
Newmarket
Suffolk CB8 8JH
Tel: 01638 661111
Fax: 01638 665789

Animal Medical Centre
Veterinary Treatment and Diagnostic Centre
242 Cricklewood Lane
London NW2 2PU
Tel: 0181 450 2228
Fax: 0181 208 1382

The Association of Chartered Physiotherapists in Animal Therapy (ACPAT)
Morland House
Salters Lane
Winchester
Hampshire SO22 5JP
Tel: 01962 844390

Association of Pet Behaviour Counsellors (APBC)
P O Box 46
Worcester WR8 9YS
Tel: 01386 751151
Fax: 01386 751151

Association of Pet Dog Trainers (APDT)
Peacock Farm, Northchapel
Petworth
West Sussex GU28 9JB
Tel: 01428 707620
Fax: 01428 708190

(Please send a stamped addressed envelope for your area list.)

The Blue Cross
Shilton Road
Burford
Oxfordshire OX18 4PF
Tel: 01993 822651
Fax: 01993 823083

(Caring for sick animals, re-homing stray and abandoned pets)

British Association of Homoeopathic Veterinary Surgeons
Alternative Veterinary Medicine Centre
Chinham House
Stanford-in-the-Vale
Faringdon
Oxfordshire SN7 8NQ
Tel: 01367 710324
Fax: 01367 718243

(Information and list of homoeopathic vets)

British Homoeopathic Association
27A Devonshire Street
London W1N 1RJ
Tel: 0171 935 2163

The British Small Animal Veterinary Association (BSAVA)
Kingsley House, Church Lane
Shurdington, Cheltenham
Gloucestershire GL51 5TQ
Tel: 01242 862994

British Union for the Abolition of Vivisection (BUAV)
16A Crane Grove
London N7 8LB
Tel: 0171 700 4888
Fax: 0171 700 0252

The British Veterinary Association (BVA)
7 Mansfield Street
London W1M 0AT
Tel: 0171 636 6541
Fax: 0171 436 2970

Canine Health Census
P O Box 1, Longnor
Derbyshire SK17 0JD
(Catherine O'Driscoll)

Canine Partners for Independence (CPI)
22 Homewell
Havant
Hampshire PO9 1EE
Tel: 01705 450156
Fax: 01705 470140

Celia Hammond Animal Trust
High Street, Wadhurst
East Sussex TN5 6AG
Tel: 01892 783820/783367
Fax: 01892 784882

(Inexpensive neutering clinics and animal rescue)

Children in Hospital and Animal Therapy Association (CHATA)
87 Longland Drive
Totteridge
London N20 8HN
Tel: 0181 445 7883
Fax: 0181 445 7883

The Cinnamon Trust
Foundry House
Foundry Square
Hayle
Cornwall TR27 4HH
Tel: 01736 757900
Fax: 01736 757101

(Helps to keep the elderly and physically weak with their pets)

Compassion in World Farming (CWF)
Charles House
5A Charles Street
Petersfield
Hampshire GU32 3EH
Tel: 01730 264208/268863
Fax: 01730 260791

Country Fairs
Woodend
Slindon Bottom Road
Fontwell, Arundel
West Sussex BN18 0SL
Tel: 01243 544181
Mobile: 0831 430608
Fax: 01243 544068

Katy Cropper
Whightwick Mill
Bridgnorth Road
Whightwick, Wolverhampton
Staffordshire WV6 0XX
Tel: 01902 765053
Mobile: 0850 896637
Fax: 01902 765052

Dogs for the Disabled
The Old Vicarage, London Road
Ryton-on-Dunsmore
Coventry CV8 3ER
Tel: 01203 302057
Fax: 01203 302041

The Dogs' Home Battersea
4 Battersea Park Road
London SW8 4AA
Tel: 0171 622 3626
Fax: 0171 622 6451

Earth Island Institute
Earth Island Journal
300 Broadway, Suite 28
San Francisco
California 94133–3312
USA
Tel: 00 1 415 788 3666
Fax: 00 1 415 788 7324

Franley Products
37 Riverside
Rawcliffe
Goole
East Yorkshire DN14 8RN
Tel: 01405 831003
Fax: 01405 839958

Makers of excellent animal accessories and suppliers of healthy animal feeds

Friends of the Earth Trust
26–28 Underwood Street
London N1 7JQ
Tel: 0171 490 1555
Fax: 0171 490 0881

Guide Dogs for the Blind Association
Hillfields
Burghfields
Reading RG7 3YG
Tel: 01734 835555
Fax: 01734 835433

Hand To Paw
North Cottage
Great Hayes
Headley Common Road
Headley
Surrey KT18 6NE
Tel: 01372 375302/0831 619847
Fax: 01372 375302

(Animal Rescue Directory)

Hearing Dogs for Deaf People
The Training Centre
London Road (A40)
Lewknor
Oxfordshire OX9 5RY
Tel: 01844 353898
Fax: 01844 353099

The Homoeopathy Society
2 Powis Place
Great Ormond Street
London WC1N 3HT
Tel: 0171 837 9469
Fax: 0171 278 7900

Institute of Trading Standards Administration
3/5 Hadleigh Business Centre
351 London Road
Hadleigh
Essex SS7 2BT
Tel: 01702 559922
Fax: 01702 559902

The Kennel Club
1–5 Clarges Street
Piccadilly
London W1A 8AB
Tel: 0171 493 6651/629 5828 (General)
Tel: 0171 493 2001 (Registration)
Tel: 01372 743472 (Insurance)
Tel: 0171 518 1099 (Library)
Fax: 0171 518 1058

(Dog Rescue Directory/Crufts)

Meat and Livestock Commission
Snowdon Drive
Winterhill, Milton Keynes
Buckinghamshire MK6 1AX
Tel: 01908 677577
Fax: 01908 609221

Ministry of Agriculture Fisheries and Food (MAFF)
Ergon House, c/o Nobel House
17 Smith Square
London SW1P 3JR
Tel: 0171 270 8080
Help Line: 0645 335577

Ministry of Agriculture, Fisheries and Food (MAFF)
Government Buildings (Toby Jug Site)
Hook Rise South
Tolworth
Surbiton
Surrey KT6 7NF
Tel: 0181 330 4411
Fax: 0181 337 3640

(List of quarantine kennels)

National Animal Welfare Trust (NAWT)
Tyler's Way
Watford By-pass
Watford
Hertfordshire WD2 8HQ
Tel: 0181 950 8215/0177

The National Anti-Vivisection Society Limited
261 Goldhawk Road
London W12 9PE
Tel: 0181 846 9777
Fax: 0181 846 9712

(Animal Defenders, The Lord Dowding Fund for Humane Research)

National Canine Defence League (NCDL)
17 Wakley Street
London EC1V 7LT
Tel: 0171 837 0006
Fax: 0171 833 2701
(NCDL's rescue centres)

National Office of Animal Health Limited (NOAH)
3 Crossfield Chambers
Gladbeck Way
Enfield
Middlesex EN2 7HF
Tel: 0181 367 3131
Fax: 0181 363 1155

The National Pet Register
Thorpe Underwood Hall
York YO5 9SZ
Tel: 0700 0800 123

(Computerised tracing for lost dogs – registration and insurance)

National Pet Week
P O Box 101
Northwood
Middlesex HA6 3RH
Tel: 0181 428 7369
Fax: 0181 428 7369

(People for Pets – Pets for People)

Passports for Pets
20 Seymour Road
London SW18 5JA
Tel: 0181 870 5960
Fax: 0181 870 9223

(The alternative to quarantine)

People for the Ethical Treatment of Animals (PETA)
P O Box 3169
London NW1 2JF
Tel: 0181 785 3113

People's Dispensary for Sick Animals (PDSA)
Whitechapel Way
Priorslee
Telford
Shropshire TF2 9PQ
Tel: 01952 290999
Fax: 01952 291035

Pet Care Trust
Bedford Business Centre
170 Mile Road
Bedford MK42 9YZ
Tel: 01234 273933
Fax: 01234 273550

The Pet Food Manufacturers' Association (PFMA)
Suite 1/2 12–13 Henrietta Street
London WC2E 8LH
Tel: 0171 379 9009
Fax: 0171 379 8008/3898

Pet Health Council
Thistledown Cottage
49 Main Street
Sewstern
Grantham
Lincolnshire NG33 5RF
Tel: 01476 861379
Fax: 01476 861336

Promoting The Value Of Dogs For The Benefit Of People And Pets As Therapy (PRO DOGS & PAT DOGS)
Rocky Bank, 4–6 New Road
Ditton, Aylesford, Maidstone
Kent ME20 6AD
Tel: 01732 872222/848499

The Protesters Animal Information Network Limited (PAIN)
The Lodge
Broadhurst Manor
Horsted Keynes
West Sussex RH17 7BG
Tel: 01342 811377
Fax: 01342 811213

(Carla Lane and Celia Hammond. Carla Lane has also set up Animal Line and Animal Rescue.)

Raystede Centre for Animal Welfare Limited
Raystede, Ringmer
East Sussex BN8 5AJ
Tel: 01825 840252

Royal College of Veterinary Surgeons
Belgravia House
62–64 Horseferry Road
London SW1P 2AF
Tel: 0171 222 2001
Fax: 0171 222 2004

Royal Society for the Prevention of Cruelty to Animals – (RSPCA)
Causeway
Horsham
West Sussex RH12 1HG
Tel: 01403 264181
Fax: 01403 241048
Cruelty Line: 0990 555999

Royal Veterinary College
Camden Campus
Royal College Street
London NW1 0TU
Tel: 0171 468 5000
Fax: 0171 388 2342

(The Beaumont Animals' Hospital Tel: 0171 387 8134)

Hawkshead Campus
Hawkshead Lane
North Mimms
Hatfield, Herts. AL9 7TA
Tel: 01707 666333
Fax: 01707 652090
(ACT – Animal Care Trust)

The Scottish Kennel Club
3 Brunswick Place
Edinburgh EH7 5HP
Tel: 0131 557 2877
Fax: 0131 556 6784

Scottish Society for the Prevention of Cruelty to Animals (SPCA)
Braehead Mains
603 Queensferry Road
Edinburgh EH4 6EA
Tel: 0131 339 0222
Fax: 0131 339 4777

Society for Companion Animals Studies (SCAS)
10B Leny Road
Callander
Scotland FK17 8BA
Tel: 01877 330996
Fax: 01877 330996

(Includes Pet Loss Advisory Group)

Soil Association
86 Colston Street
Bristol BS1 5BB
Tel: 0117 929 0661
Fax: 0117 925 2504

(Directory of organic farm shops and box schemes)

Support Dogs
P O Box 447
Sheffield S6 6YZ
Tel: 0114 232 0026
Fax: 0114 232 0026

Therapaws
The Canine Therapeutic and Leisure Swimming Pool
Street End Lane
Sidlesham, Chichester
West Sussex PO20 7RG
Tel: 01243 641114

Ulster Society for the Prevention of Cruelty to Animals (USPCA)
Unit 4, Boucher Business Centre
Apollo Road
Belfast BT12 6HP
Tel: 01232 660479
Fax: 01232 381911
Animal Helpline: 0990 134329

Vegan Society
Donald Watson House
7 Battle Road
St Leonards-on-Sea
East Sussex TN37 7AA
Tel: 01424 427393
Fax: 01424 717064

Vegetarian Society
Parkdale
Dunham Road
Altrincham
Cheshire WA14 4QG
Tel: 0161 928 0793
Fax: 0161 926 9182

Which?
P O Box 44
Hertford SG14 1SH
Tel: 01992 822800
Fax: 0171 830 8585

World Society for the Protection of Animals
2 Langley Lane
London SW8 1TJ
Tel: 0171 793 0540
Fax: 0171 793 0208

NOTABLE NAMES

Mr Trevor Adams BVSc CertBR VetMFHom MRCVS
The Orchard Veterinary Surgery
King Street, Glastonbury
Somerset BA6 9JX
Tel: 01458 832972

(Homoeopathic vet.)

Mr Richard Allport BVetMed VetMFHom MRCVS
Natural Medicine Veterinary Centre
11 Southgate Road, Potters Bar
Hertfordshire EN6 5DR
Tel: 01701 662058
Fax: 01701 646948

(Referral service in: acupuncture, Bach flower therapy, electro crystal therapy, homoeopathy, healing, herbal medicine, aromatherapy, physiotherapy, massage, osteopathy and behaviour counselling and promotes a large range of natural products.) See Animal Actives in Preferred Products.

Dr Ian Billinghurst
P O Box 703
Lithgow
New South Wales 2790
Australia

(Noted Australian vet, author of *Give Your Dog A Bone*.)

Katie Boyle
c/o J. Gurnett Ltd
2 New Kings Road
London SW6 4SA
Tel: 0171 736 7828

(Author of *Battersea Tails*, Agony Aunt on *Dogs Today*, on the Committee of Management of The Dogs' Home Battersea for over twenty years, Patron of National Canine Defence League, Animal Health Trust and Animal Welfare Trust.)

Mr Keith Butt MA VetMB MRCVS
8 Kynance Mews
Gloucester Road
London SW7 4QP
Tel: 0171 584 2019

(A London general vet who was brilliant with Blue, my Dobermann who had hip dysplasia. His particular interests are skin and cancer.)

Mr John Carter BVetMed MRCVS
290 Kenton Road
Harrow
Middlesex HA3 8DD
Tel: 0181 907 6051

(Specialises in cancer and leukaemia. Good success rates.)

Mr Timothy Couzens BVetMed MRCVS VetMFHom
Holistic Veterinary Medicine Centre
The Village Works, London Road
East Hoathly, Lewes
East Sussex BN8 6QA
Tel: 01825 840966

(Homoeopathic vet.)

Mr Christopher Day MA VetMB VetMFHom MRCVS
Alternative Veterinary Medicine Centre
Chinham House, Stanford-in-the-Vale
Faringdon
Oxfordshire SN7 8NQ
Tel: 01367 710324

(Homoeopathic vet.)

Juliette de Bairacli Levy
(Extremely knowledgeable on herbs and homoeopathy and nutrition for different dogs. Author of *The Complete Herbal Handbook For the Dog and Cat*.)

Dr Ian Dunbar BVetMed BSc PhD
Center for Applied Animal Behaviour
2140 Shattuck Avenue #2406
Berkeley
California 94704
USA
Tel: 00 1 510 658 8588

(The television vet – *Dogs With Dunbar* – and expert on dog behaviour.)

Mr Mark Elliott BVSc VetMFHom MRCVS
Kingley Veterinary Centre
Oldwick Farm, West Stoke Road
Lavant, Nr Chichester
West Sussex PO18 9AA
Tel: 01243 528899
Fax: 01243 528877

(Our homoeopathic/ acupuncturist vet and adviser.)

Dr Bruce Fogle DVM(Gu) MRCVS
86 York Street
London W1H 1DP
Tel: 0171 723 2068

(Excellent vet, journalist and author of superb dog books including *First Aid for Dogs, 101 Essential Tips Caring for Your Dog, The Dog Encyclopedia*.)

Mr Peter Graham Goodrich BVetMed VetMFHom MRCVS
Kingston House
85 Main Street
Pembroke
Dyfed SA71 4DB
Tel: 01646 622943

(Homoeopathic vet.)

Mr Peter Gregory BVSc VetMFHom MRCVS
6 Queen Street
Newcastle under Lyme
Staffordshire ST5 1ED
Tel: 01782 719771

(Homoeopathic vet.)

Celia Hammond
High Street, Wadhurst
East Sussex TN5 6AG
Tel: 01892 783820/783367
Fax: 01892 784882

(Founder of inexpensive neutering and spaying clinics for dogs and cats.)

Mr John Hoare BVSc VetMFHom MRCVS
12 Martins Road
Hanham, Bristol
Avon BS15 3EW
Tel: 0117 967 7067

(Homoeopathic vet.)

Mr Francis Hunter VetMFHom MRCVS
Arun Veterinary Group
121 Lower Street
Pulborough
West Sussex RH20 2BP
Tel: 01798 872089

(Homoeopathic vet – Chairman of the British Homoeopathic Association, a charity whose aim is to promote homoeopathy for people and animals; former president of the British Association of Homoeopathic Veterinary Surgeons.)

Mrs Barbara Jones BVMS VetMFHom MRCVS
Oakwood Veterinary Centre
Babbinswood Farm
Whittington, Oswestry
Shropshire SY11 4PH
Tel: 01691 679699

(Homoeopathic vet and canine acupuncturist.)

Mr Richard Lockyer BVMS VetMFHom MRCVS
Highfield Veterinary Surgery
White Stubbs Lane
Broxbourne
Hertfordshire EN10 7QA
Tel: 01992 440738

(Homoeopathic vet.)

Mr Tom Lonsdale BVetMed MRCVS
Riverstone Veterinary Hospital
Garfield Road
Riverstone
New South Wales 2765
Australia

Catherine O'Driscoll
PO Box 1
Longnor
Derbyshire SK17 0JD

(Instigator of the Canine Health Census, author of *Who Killed the Darling Buds of May?* which is about vaccinations, runs Abbeywood Publishing Ltd – please send s.a.e. for details)

Dr Richard H Pitcairn, DVM, Ph.D.
Director
1283 Lincoln Street
Eugene
Oregon 97401
USA
Tel: 00 1 503 342 7665

(Co-author of *Dr Pitcairn's Complete Guide to Natural Health for Dogs and Cats*.)

Mr John Saxton BVetMed VetMFHom MRCVS
Tower Wood Veterinary Group
27 Tinshill Road
Leeds LS16 7DR
Tel: 01132 678419

(Homoeopathic vet.)

Miss Christine Shields BVSc VetMFHom MRCVS
43 Main Street
Warton, Carnforth
Lancashire LA5 9NT
Tel: 01524 736765

(Homoeopathic vet.)

William George Smith
29 Elm Road
Westergate, Chichester
West Sussex PO20 6RQ
Tel: 01243 543991

(Spiritual healer.)

Mrs June Third-Carter BVMS VetMFHom MRCVS
Hillhead House
Lonmay, By Fraserburgh
Aberdeenshire AB43 4UP
Tel: 01346 532948

(Homoeopathic vet.)

Mrs Susan Thomas MA VetMB VetMFHom MRCVS
Tower Wood Veterinary Group
27 Tinshill Road
Leeds LS16 7DR
Tel: 01132 678419

(Homoeopathic vet.)

BIBLIOGRAPHY

CANINE CARE

Mad Cow Disease and the Risk to Mankind
Brian J. Ford
Corgi Books, 1996

Canine Nutrition and Choosing the Best Food for Your Breed of Dog
William D. Cusick
Adele Publications, 1990

Clinical Nutrition of the Dog and Cat
J.W. Simpson, R.S. Anderson, P.J. Markwell
Blackwell Scientific Publications, 1993

The Complete Book of Dog Care
Tim Harcroft
Ringpress Books, 1992

Dr Pitcairn's Complete Guide to Natural Health for Dogs and Cats
Richard H. Pitcairn and Susan Hubble Pitcairn
Rodale Press 1995

The Doctor's Book of Home Remedies for Dogs and Cats
By the editors of *Prevention* Magazine Health Books
Edited by Matthew Hoffman
Rodale Press, 1996

Do Dogs Need Shrinks?
Dr Peter Neville
Pan Books, 1993

The Dog
The Complete Guide to Dogs and Their World
David Alderton
Quill Publishing, 1987

Dogs and Homoeopathy, the Owner's Companion
Mark Elliott and Tony Pinkus
Ainsworths Homoeopathic Pharmacy, 1996

Dogs: Homoeopathic Remedies
George Macleod
The C.W. Daniel Co.

Dogs Never Lie About Love
Reflections on the Emotional World of Dogs
Jeffrey Mason
Jonathan Cape, 1997

Give Your Dog a Bone
Dr Ian Billinghurst
available in the UK from Abbeywood Publishing

Heal Your Dog the Natural Way
Richard Allport
Mitchell Beazley, 1997

How to Care for Your Older Dog
Bill Landesman and Kathleen Berman
New English Library, 1978

Immune for Life
Live Longer and Better by Strengthening Your 'Doctor Within'
Arnold Fox, MD and Barry Fox
Prima Publishing, 1990

In Accord with Nature
A Comprehensive Guide to Giving Your Dog a Healthy Lifestyle
Denes Natural Pet Care

Natural Healing for Dogs and Cats
Diane Stein
The Crossing Press, 1993

Natural Health, Natural Medicine
Andrew Weil, MD
Warner Books, 1997

The Natural Remedy Book for Dogs and Cats
Diane Stein
The Crossing Press, 1994

101 Essential Tips Caring for Your Dog
Dr Bruce Fogle
Dorling Kindersley, 1995

Who Killed the Darling Buds of May?
1: Vaccination – What Vets Don't Tell You About Vaccines
Catherine O'Driscoll
Abbeywood Publishing (Vaccines) Ltd, 1997

You and Your Dog
The Complete Owner's Guide to Dogs: their Care, Health and Behaviour
David Taylor with Peter Scott
Dorling Kindersley, 1994

You Don't Have to Feel Unwell!
Nutrition, Lifestyle, Herbs and Homoeopathy
Robin Needes
Gateway Books, 1994

CANINE CUISINE

About Macrobiotics
The Ways of Eating
Craig Sams
Thorsons, 1983

Friends of the Earth Cookbook
Veronica Sekules
Penguin, 1981

The Kind Food Guide
Audrey Eyton
Penguin

The Practically Macrobiotic Cookbook
Preparation of more than 200 delicious recipes
Keith Michell
Thorsons, 1987

The Vegan Cookbook
Alan Wakeman and Gordon Baskerville
Faber and Faber, 1996

CANINE FACT AND FICTION

Animal Verse
compiled by Raymond Wilson
Beaver Books, 1982

Brewer's Dictionary of Phrase and Fable
Ivor H. Evans
Cassells, 1988

The Call of the Wild, White Fang and Other Stories
Jack London
Penguin, 1983

Dictionary of Quotations
Bloomsbury, 1987

The Dog in Art From Rococo to Post Modernism
Robert Rosenblum
John Murray, 1988

Dogs
Armard Eisen
Ariel Books, 1992

Far From the Madding Crowd
Thomas Hardy
Mammoth [first published 1874]

The Hound of the Baskervilles
Conan Doyle
Oxford University Press, 1993

Lady's Maid
Margaret Forster
Chatto & Windus, 1990

The Literary Companion to Dogs
Christopher Hawtree
Sinclair-Stevenson, 1993

Mother Goose's Nursery Rhymes
edited by L. Edna Walter
A.&C. Black, 1951 [original 1924]

The New English Bible – New Testament
Oxford University Press
Cambridge University Press, 1961

100 Favourite Animal Poems
chosen by Laurence Cotterell
Judy Piatkus, 1992

The Penguin Book of Animal Verse
Edited by George MacBeth
Penguin, 1965

Peter Pan
J. M. Barrie
Everyman's Library Children's Classics, 1992
[original 1911]

The Pickwick Papers
Charles Dickens
Penguin, 1986 [original 1836]

Rebecca
Daphne du Maurier
Arrow, 1997 [first published 1938]

Sussex Seams – a Collection of Travel Writing
Edited by Paul Foster
Alan Sutton, 1996

The Wizard of Oz
L. Frank Baum
Puffin, 1982 [original 1900]

LITERARY ACKNOWLEDGEMENTS

Acknowledgement and thanks are due to the following for kindly giving us permission to reproduce or make reference to copyright material:

Richard Allport BVetMed VetMFHom MRCVS: references to material in his leaflet 'Animal Actives' and his book *Heal Your Dog the Natural Way*.

Amanda Barton-Chapple: poem 'What I Love About My Dog Tippy' from *Never, Grandma, Never*.

Timothy Couzens BVetMed VetMFHom MRCVS: reference to his article 'Controlling Fleas' in the magazine *Pet Dogs*, April 1997.

Extract from *Rebecca* by Daphne du Maurier, reproduced with permission of Curtis Brown Ltd, London, on behalf of The Chichester Partnership. Copyright © Daphne du Maurier 1938.

Dr Hugo Donnelly: extract from 'Waiting' in *Sussex Seams* (a collection of travel writing) edited by Paul Foster, published by Alan Sutton Publishing Ltd. Copyright © Paul Foster and the individual contributors, 1996.

Mark Elliott BVSc VetMFHom MRCVS and Tony Pinkus BPharm MRPharmS: material from *Dogs Homoeopathy, The Owner's Companion*. © M. Elliott and T. Pinkus 1996.

Faber and Faber Ltd: extracts from *The Complete Herbal Handbook For the Dog and Cat* by Juliette de Bairacli Levy.

Excerpt from *Peter Pan* by J. M. Barrie by permission of Great Ormond Street Children's Hospital.

Christopher Hampton: quote from the *Sunday Times* Magazine (16 October 1977).

Lynne Hill, Veterinary Affairs Manager at Hill's Pet Nutrition: quote from 'News From Hill's' from *Dogs for the Disabled Newsletter*, Issue 19, October 1996.

One extract from *The Incredible Journey* by Sheila Burnford reproduced by permission of Hodder and Stoughton Ltd. Copyright © 1960 Sheila Burnford.

Francis Hunter VetMFHom MRCVS: information on worming and his homoeopathic remedy for diabetes.

Macmillan: extract from the poem 'A Popular Personage at Home' from *The Complete Poems* by Thomas Hardy, ed. James Gibson, published by Papermac, 1976; extract from *Far From the Madding Crowd* by Thomas Hardy, published by Papermac, 1976.

Keith Michell: extract from *The Practically Macrobiotic Cookbook*, published by Thorsons Publishing Group. © Keith Michell 1987.

John Murray (Publishers) Ltd: extract from *The Letters of Elizabeth Barrett Browning to Mary Russell Mitford 1836–54* (volume II) edited and introduced by Meredith B. Raymond and Mary Rose Sullivan. Copyright © Browning Letters, John Murray, 1983; extract from *The Hound of the Baskervilles* by Arthur Conan Doyle.

Catherine O'Driscoll: reference to material in her book, *Who Killed the Darling Buds of May? – What Vets Don't Tell You About Vaccines*, published by Abbeywood Publishing (Vaccines) Ltd, 1997.

Random House UK Ltd: extract from *Space Dog the Hero* by Natalie

Standiford, published by Hutchinson Children's Books; extracts from *Lady's Maid* by Margaret Forster, published by Chatto & Windus. Copyright © Margaret Forster 1990.

Gar Smith, editor of *Earth Island Journal* (San Francisco, California USA): reference to the articles 'The Truth About Cats and Dogs' by Ann Martin and 'Food Not Fit For a Pet' by Dr Wendell O. Belfield DVM, which appeared in *Earth Island Journal* volume 11, number 3, summer 1996; *The Dark Side of Recycling*, Fall 1990.

The Society of Authors as the literary representative of the Estate of Virginia Woolf: extract from *On a Faithful Friend* by Virginia Woolf, the *Guardian*, 18 January 1905.

Every reasonable care has been taken to trace ownership of copyrighted material. Information that will enable the publishers to rectify any reference or credit is welcome.

'I pray you who own me, let me continue to live close to Nature. Know that: I love to run beneath the sun, the moon and the stars; I need to feel the storm winds around me, and the touch of rain, hail, sleet and snow; I need to splash in streams and brooks, and to swim in ponds, lakes, rivers and seas; I need to be allowed to retain my kinship with Nature.'

Juliette de Bairacli Levy
from *The Complete Herbal Handbook for the Dog and Cat*

'Stop running those dogs on your page. I wouldn't have them peeing on my cheapest rug.'

William Randolph Hearst
from *Dictionary of Quotations*

(Referring to the publication of James Thurber's drawings by one of his editors.)

THE END